Fumitories of Britain and Ireland

B.S.B.I. Handbook No. 12

Rosaline J. Murphy

with the assistance of
Ian Bennallick and Alex Lockton

Edited by
Tim Rich
National Museum of Wales

Botanical Society of the British Isles
London

2009

Fumitories of Britain and Ireland
B.S.B.I. Handbook No. 12
Rosaline J. Murphy

Published by the
Botanical Society of the British Isles
c/o The Botany Department
Natural History Museum
Cromwell Road
London
SW7 5BD

www.bsbi.org.uk

2009

ISBN 13: 978-0-901158-40-6

Cover design by Oscar Klappholz.

Cover picture: *Fumaria purpurea*, cultivated in Cardiff from Orkney material.

Contents

Preface and acknowledgements

This handbook is dedicated to Herbert William Pugsley (1868-1947), whose detailed work on *Fumaria* laid the foundations of our knowledge today.

My first introduction to fumitories was on a field trip to The Lizard when I was shown *F. bastardii* and was told how it could be recognised. At that time I did not realise that I was seeing *F. bastardii* var. *bastardii* – that knowledge was to come later. With retirement and subsequent appointment as BSBI Recorder for v.c. 2 (East Cornwall), I found myself leading many field trips in Cornwall. Always there were requests to see *F. occidentalis*, *F. purpurea* and the rare *F. martinii* (now *F. reuteri*). This led to the next stage, the steep learning curve that is always associated with critical plants, even with a genus like *Fumaria*, where British species are so few, yet flowers and fruits in some instances are so similar.

The first monograph of British and Irish *Fumaria* was produced by H.W. Pugsley in 1912, and many of the names (although admittedly not all) that he gave to the species, subspecies, varieties and forms still stand today. However, in further works by different authors, descriptions were restricted to species or, at the most, subspecies. Few mentioned the amazing number of small differences that could be seen when plants were examined in detail. A guide that dealt with these problems and illustrated them with drawings and photographs seemed to be needed. At the same time, such a guide would allow for the lengthened descriptions that often provide just that extra clue that allows one to be certain of a plant's identification. The outline of the proposed book was taken to the BSBI's Publications Committee in 2007 and it was accepted as the first in a series of mini-handbooks covering small genera that are difficult to identify.

These species accounts are based on personal observations of material in the field, either collected by me or by others, descriptions in the literature (especially those by Pugsley, Daker, Sell and Lidén), and herbarium material. Peter Sell kindly made available the draft account of *Fumaria* from his forthcoming *Flora of Great Britain and Ireland*. The line drawings are either by E.W. Hunnybun (slightly modified in layout and content) or by me. The original drawings made by Hunnybun for the *Cambridge British Flora* (Moss 1920) are held in the herbarium at the University of Cambridge, and copies may also be seen with the appropriate species in the British Herbarium at the Natural History Museum. My drawings are all to scale and have been drawn using a stereo-microscope. The photographs show flowers and fruits in detail, whole inflorescences, and plants in their habitats. The photographs were taken by T. Rich unless otherwise stated.

This handbook has been put together with the help of Ian Bennallick, Alex Lockton, Tim Rich and Martin and Katherine Sanford, to whom I extend my grateful thanks.

I would also like to thank the Keepers of the Natural History Museum (BM), the National Museum of Wales (NMW) and Launceston Museum (LAUS) for loan of, or access to, material; and to the following for their help: Paul Ashton, Arthur Chater, Michael Daker, Ruth Dawes, Mike Foley, Colin French, Paul Gainey, Paul Green, Brian Laney, Geoffrey Halliday, David Holyoak, John Humphreys, Richard Lansdown, Ruth Lees, Alan Leslie, Heather McHaffie, Len Margetts, Hazel Meredith, Tony Mundell, Philip Oswald, Rosemary Parslow, David Pearman, Colin Pope, Chris Preston, Kath & Richard Pryce, Nicholas de Sausmarez, Alan Showler, Clive Stace, Nick Stewart, Matt Stribley, Geoff Toone, James Turner, Roger Veall, Sarah Whild, Phil Wilson and Mike Wyse Jackson. I would like to thank the BSBI vice-county recorders who have helped update the list of vice-counties for which the various taxa have been recorded.

Finally, I would like to thank the BSBI for publishing this handbook.

Rose Murphy, 2008

Introduction

Fumitories are a fascinating group of plants. They have such very distinctive flowers that it seems surprising that they were once included with poppies in the Papaveraceae. Recent molecular evidence, however, has given support to their recognition in a separate family, the Fumariaceae (Jonsell 2001; Stace 1997; Lidén 2002). It is a family that, in Britain and Ireland, includes *Fumaria* with *Dicentra*, *Ceratocapnos*, *Corydalis* and *Pseudofumaria*.

There are about 60 species in the genus *Fumaria*. Many of them are found around the Mediterranean, some extending into central Europe, and others further west. Some may be found in India and a few in the mountains of East Africa. A number have also become naturalised as weeds in other temperate regions of the world. In Britain and Ireland there are 10 species, including two endemics, *F. purpurea* and *F. occidentalis*.

In this account the genus is subdivided into two sections: section *Fumaria* and section *Capreolatae* Hammar, following Lidén (1986). Pugsley (1912) gave more detailed subdivisions, and it may be that these will still prove of value as further phylogenetic studies are made within the genus.

Members of the section *Fumaria* are, with the exception of *F. officinalis*, more common in the east of Britain and Ireland. These are the small-flowered species (flowers 9 mm or less). They have narrower leaf-segments that are lanceolate or linear and flat or channelled. The upper petals of their flowers have broad margins or wings that are more or less patent, while the lower petals are spathulate. Their pollen grains have more than six pores. All are classed as archaeophytes, that is species introduced to this country by man before 1500. The two rarest species, *F. parviflora* and *F. vaillantii* are almost confined to the chalk of South-east England and are absent from Ireland, while *F. officinalis* subsp. *wirtgenii* and *F. densiflora* are rare in Ireland. The centre of diversity for this group is somewhat eastern (Lidén 1986).

Section *Capreolatae* includes the large-flowered fumitories (flowers 9 mm or more). Members of this group are considered to be native and are largely western in their distribution in Britain and scattered in Ireland. Their leaf segments are flat and relatively wide, while the upper petals of their flowers have wings that are turned upwards and their lower petals are very rarely spathulate. Biochemically, their chromatograms show a coptisine spot, recognised by its greenish-yellow colour. Their pollen grains have six pores (hexaporate). The centre of diversity for this group is N.W. Africa (Lidén 1986).

It is likely that all species are self-compatible and largely automatically self-pollinating, though this has not been tested experimentally for all species. In young buds and flowers, the stamens and style are positioned together. As the style grows it passes between the anthers, collecting pollen on the stigma, thus effecting self-pollination even before the flowers mature. Flowers may also be visited by insects, but they are rarely recorded doing so. It is likely that this habitual self-pollination is responsible for the commonly observed patterns of morphological variation where there is a myriad of locally distinct forms, some of which have received taxonomic recognition. Whether these self-pollinating forms will be maintained in the light of experimental analysis remains to be seen.

The order in which the species are given here follows Lidén (1986).

Section *Capreolatae*

1. *Fumaria capreolata* L.
   (a) subsp. *capreolata*
   (b) subsp. *babingtonii* (Pugsley) P.D. Sell
2. *Fumaria occidentalis* Pugsley
3. *Fumaria bastardii* Boreau
4. *Fumaria reuteri* Boiss
5. *Fumaria muralis* Sond. ex W.D.J. Koch
   (a) subsp. *muralis*
   (b) subsp. *boraei* (Jord.) Pugsley
   (c) subsp. *neglecta* Pugsley
6. *Fumaria purpurea* Pugsley

Section *Fumaria*

7. *Fumaria officinalis* L.
   (a) subsp. *officinalis*
   (b) subsp. *wirtgenii* (W.D.J. Koch) Arcang.
8. *Fumaria densiflora* DC.
9. *Fumaria parviflora* Lam.
10. *Fumaria vaillantii* Loisel.

Fumitories have often been considered difficult to name, perhaps due to their tendency to show a fair degree of variation and the ease with which they produce cleistogamous flowers, the latter making individuals with them almost impossible to identify. Many of the variants have been given names; Pugsley (1912, 1920) listed 23 infraspecific taxa, and 20 of them can still be found in the present literature either as varieties or forms (Sell 1998).

A number of these variants can be named only with experience, and some, like *F. muralis* subsp. *boraei* var. *ambigua*, have not been recorded for many years. As identification can be difficult, two keys are provided. Key A allows the identification of species and subspecies. Key B is more detailed and it includes varieties and forms. Both keys are dichotomous but provide extra information where this will help with the identification.

All species and some subspecies and varieties are illustrated using photographs and drawings. Three special drawings are included, which illustrate the differences between pairs of taxa that can be confused: *F. capreolata* and *F. occidentalis* (Figure 16); *F. capreolata* and *F. purpurea* (Figure 58); and *F. muralis* subsp. *boraei* and *F. purpurea* (Figure 51). A drawing that compares the flowers and sepals of the five archaeophytes that occur in Britain is also included (Figure 70).

Distribution maps are given for all species. The maps show the most recent (post 2000) records as large dots – displayed as 8km circles centred on the recording units of the 10km × 10km squares of the Ordnance Survey national grid for Britain and the equivalents for Ireland and the Channel Isles. Where there is no recent record, progressively smaller dots are given in four additional date classes as shown in the key here. The data are derived from numerous sources, including the Biological Records Centre at Wallingford, the BSBI's members and vice-county recorders, and many literature sources and herbarium specimens (Figure 1). When using the maps it is important to bear in mind that coverage is not comprehensive in any date class.

Key to map symbols

● 2000+
● 1987-1999
● 1970-1986
● 1930-1969
• -1929

IUCN threat statuses follow Cheffings & Farrell (2005) for Britain, and provisional statuses are given for Ireland, where they are currently under review.

Hybrids between species of *Fumaria* seem to be rare in the wild and there are few records. Four hybrids have been recorded. For *F. bastardii* × *muralis* and *F. officinalis* × *parviflora* only one record exists. There are more records for *F. muralis* subsp. *boraei* × *officinalis* (= *F.* × *painteri* Pugsley) and *F. officinalis* × *densiflora*. Wilson *et al.* (1990) obtained a range of hybrids in cultivation by artificial cross-pollination.

Two species of *Fumaria,* one native to northern France (*F. caroliana* Pugsley) and the other native to the Mediterranean (*F. agraria* Lag.) have been recorded as non-persistent casuals in East and South-east England. They are discussed and described separately after the other species.

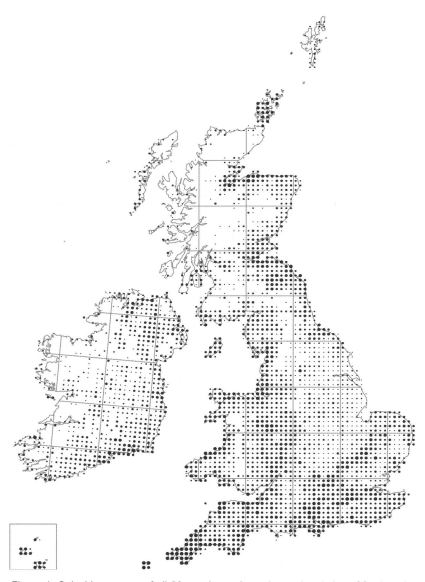

Figure 1. Coincidence map of all 22 species, subspecies and varieties of fumitory in Britain and Ireland, showing larger dots for more taxa recorded in a 10km square (the largest number is 9). The map gives some indication of the recording coverage and of the distribution of the genus.

Characters important for identification

Most accounts of *Fumaria* place great emphasis on the need for fully-developed flowers and ripe, dry fruits for identification (Lidén 1986, 2002; Sell 1998). Other characters may also be useful, such as the ratio of sepal to corolla size, and the angle of the fruiting pedicels.

Fumitories are, however, very variable phenotypically and modifications to both leaves and flowers occur due to shade, the type of habitat, drought and the season of the year. The length of the peduncle in proportion to the raceme, and the length of the bracts in relation to the fruiting pedicel, feature both in some keys and in species descriptions, but these characters may vary between and within species. Care is therefore needed when interpreting their form. Added to this is the problem of the differences that named varieties exhibit when compared with the more common and often more widespread form of the species or subspecies. There are also some undescribed local forms. Reliance on any one particular character can thus be misleading.

The basic structure of a fumitory is first described below, followed by more detailed descriptions of the characters.

The basic structure of fumitories

Fumitories are glabrous, sometimes glaucous, annual plants. They may be erect or suberect, diffuse or climb by means of cirrhose (coiling) petioles (they lack tendrils). Their stems are often well-branched from the base, or above. The leaves are alternate, the upper ones are often sessile. Most leaves are 2–3(–4)-pinnatisect, but in young plants the basal leaves are 2–3-ternate. The ultimate leaf segments, wide or narrow, are usually flat but in some species they are very fine, almost linear, and folded upwards so that they appear channelled.

The racemes are leaf-opposed, and may be pedunculate, subsessile or sessile.

The basic structure of a fumitory flower is shown in Figure 2. Each flower on the raceme is born on a short pedicel that often becomes much thickened after fertilisation. The pedicels have a bract at their base.

The two sepals, one on each side of the flower, are dentate or ± entire, linear, ovate or oblong in shape, variable in size, and scarious. They sometimes fall early (caducous), one of the reasons why each fumitory plant sent for identification must be placed in a separate bag else the sepals from different plants will get confused. In some instances the sepals are more persistent and remain on each side of the developing fruits.

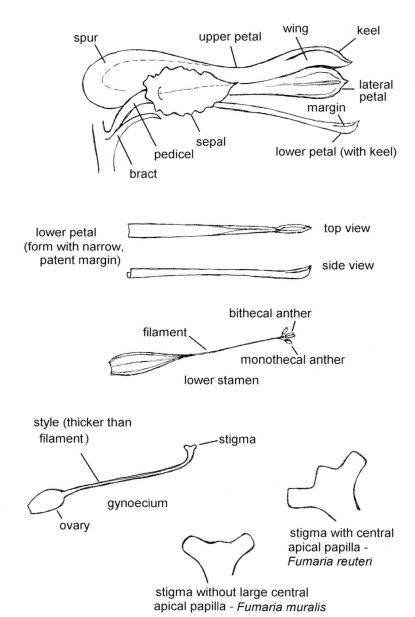

spur

upper petal

wing

keel

lateral petal

margin

lower petal (with keel)

sepal

pedicel

bract

lower petal (form with narrow, patent margin)

top view

side view

bithecal anther

filament

monothecal anther

lower stamen

style (thicker than filament)

stigma

gynoecium

ovary

stigma with central apical papilla - *Fumaria reuteri*

stigma without large central apical papilla - *Fumaria muralis*

Figure 2. Structure of *Fumaria* flowers.

Each white, pink or purplish zygomorphic flower has four petals. The upper, larger petal has a sac-like, nectar-producing spur at its base, while at its apex there is a well-marked keel or ridge along the dorsal mid-line. On each side of the keel the edges of the petal are deflexed upwards to form wings that can be very marked in some species. The two inner, lateral petals, one on each side, are dark-tipped, while the narrower lower petal, always keeled, is sometimes spathulate. All *Fumaria* species except the Moroccan *F. macrosepala* have a patent margin to the lower petal, but this can vary from being almost non-existent to very broad and it is this variation that has given rise to the idea of erect as opposed to patent margins (Lidén 1986). The inner, lateral petals are fused right at the tip of the dark-coloured area. Between these will be found the stigma with its style, and the anthers of the two stamens, upper and lower. Each stamen is really a fusion of three stamens, the anthers are therefore also a group of three with only the central one bithecal (bilobed). The upper stamen ends in a basal nectary that projects back into the spur of the upper petal. The stigmas in British and Irish species are transversely oblong with a large papilla at each side, except in *F. reuteri*, where the stigma also has a large, central, apical papilla between the two lateral ones.

The one-seeded, dry-walled, indehiscent fruits may be wider than long as in *F. officinalis* subsp. *officinalis*, or ± globose, with an apex that is emarginate, rounded, acute or apiculate. As the fruits dry, an apical pit can be seen on each side of the caducous style. In some species the fruit wall is always smooth, but in others it becomes quite rugose or even tuberculate, a character that can be seen only when the fruit wall dries. In some species, as in *F. occidentalis*, there is a marked ridge or keel that runs from each side of the fruits into the style base.

On germination, two strap-shaped cotyledons are produced. They are followed by the first true leaves which are 2–3-ternate in contrast to the later 2–3(–4)-pinnatisect leaves.

1. Sepals

Sepals vary in length from 0·5–7·0 mm, the former measurement being the smallest size seen in *F. parviflora* and *F. vaillantii*, and the latter being the largest size seen in *F. capreolata* and *F. purpurea* (Figure 3). The sepals here are measured from the base to the tip, including the teeth (Sell 1998; Rich 2006). In his keys M.G. Daker (1964, 1981) gives sepal length measurements from the point of attachment to the apex, which may give a difference of about 1 mm in length. Some authors do not state how sepals are measured.

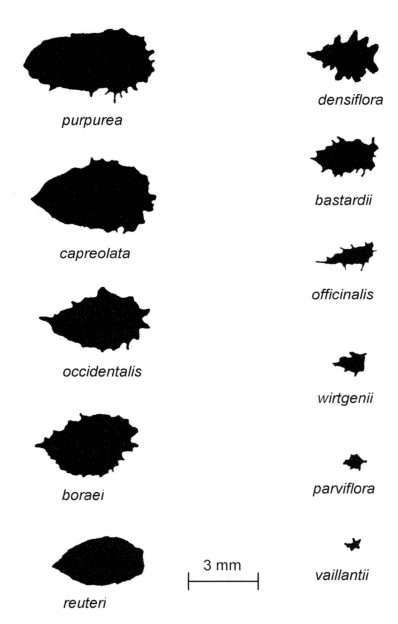

Figure 3. Sepals (after Daker 1981).

Another difficulty lies with measurements made on herbarium specimens. Measurements tend to be shorter than in fresh material as the sepals shrink, sometimes markedly so. Information from the literature may give measurements that disagree with one's own observations. Sepal length in *F. densiflora* is usually given as 2–3(–3·5) mm (Stace 1997; Lidén 2002), but Spiers (2004) found some plants where the sepal lengths reached 5 mm. With such variation, the identification clue then lies in the shape of the sepal:

- In *F. densiflora* the sepals are orbicular, dentate and wider than the breadth of the corolla.

- Small (usually 3·5 mm or less long), somewhat narrow, dentate/serrate sepals are seen in *F. vaillantii*, *F. parviflora*, *F. officinalis* and *F. bastardii*.

- Larger (2·7–5·0(–5·5) mm), ovate, dentate/serrate sepals occur in *F. occidentalis* and *F. muralis*.

- Ovate, subentire sepals are found in *F. reuteri*, *F. muralis* subsp. *neglecta* and *F. muralis* subsp. *muralis* var. *cornubiensis*, those in *F. reuteri* being the larger, to 5·0 mm long.

The biggest sepals occur in *F. capreolata* and the common form of *F. purpurea*. The shape here is either oval-oblong or oblong. In both species the mid-vein of the sepals can be green and sometimes quite wide. They are also slightly dentate or subentire. In both *F. capreolata* and *F. purpurea* the sepal is half as long as the corolla or even more, but occasionally in *F. capreolata* the sepals can be less than half as long as the corolla. In the very rare *F. purpurea* var. *brevisepala*, mentioned by Pugsley (1912, 1920), the sepals are much shorter and more like those of *F. muralis* subsp. *boraei*.

2. Corollas

The colour, length and shape of the upper petal, particularly the wings, and the form of the lower petal provide important characters for identification. The inner, lateral petals are not useful.

Most keys to fumitories start by separating the small-flowered species (section *Fumaria* – flowers 9 mm or less) from those that are large-flowered (section *Capreolatae* – flowers 9 mm or more). Apart from the pale, small (often only 8 mm or less) cleistogamous flowers produced in shade or at the end of the season, this first step in identification is usually easy.

Corolla length should be measured on mature flowers. In immature flowers the lower petal is usually held up against the lateral petals. In a mature flower the lower petal drops slightly and often extends beyond the lateral petals. The length of the flower is measured from the end of the spur to the free end (apex) of the upper petal (Figure 4); the lower petal can be ignored for the purposes of measuring flower length. Measure a few (3–5) of the longest, freshest flowers to get an estimate of the variation in flower length.

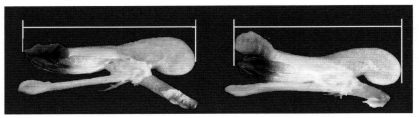

Figure 4. Measuring length of flower (*Fumaria officinalis*, Royston, v.c. 29).

In section *Capreolatae*, the largest flowers are seen in *F. occidentalis*, *F. capreolata* and *F. purpurea*, the length sometimes being as much as 15 mm. In the large-flowered fumitories, the wings of the upper petal are folded upwards, one on each side of the keel, and can be diagnostic. In *F. capreolata* the wings are low and the greenish keel, humped in appearance, is readily visible when the flower is viewed from the side. **This character cannot be seen when the flower ages and collapses**. In *F. purpurea* the wings are larger and obscure the keel. In *F. occidentalis* the most important feature is the colour of the wings. The wings start off white in the young flower, then the dark reddish hue begins to appear, creating at this stage a white margin to the wing. Finally all traces of white disappear and the flower is entirely flushed red or partly blackish-red. In bright sunlight this colour change is very marked but in shade it may fail to appear.

Colour can be a very useful guide in some fumitories when the flowers are younger and fertilisation has not yet taken place. Care is needed however as there are some local variations and differences in some varieties and forms:

- Salmon-pink, uniformly coloured upper petal
....*F. bastardii* var. *bastardii*

- Pale to rose-pink with blackish-red tips to upper
and lateral petals ....*F. muralis* subsp. *boraei*

- Creamy-white with very contrasting dark blackish tips to
upper and lateral petals .... *F. capreolata*

- Clear, almost transparent white with white margin to the
dark reddish wings of upper petal.. *F. occidentalis*

- Light purplish-pink with dark blackish-purple tips to upper
and lateral petals ....*F. purpurea*

- Almost shocking pink with conspicuous pinkish-white
sepals .... *F. densiflora*

After fertilisation, flower colour can change in some species and they may become streaked with pink or even darker. At this stage *F. capreolata* can be mistaken for *F. purpurea*, especially as the keel may cease to be obvious, but the latter species goes a dusky purple as it ages and the broad, hanging flowers clump together to give an appearance quite unlike the neat, narrow inflorescence of *F. capreolata* with its strongly deflexed flowers.

In British and Irish fumitories the margins of the lower petal are always patent (Lidén 1986). In *F. bastardii*, *F. capreolata*, *F. muralis*, *F. purpurea* and *F. reuteri* the margins at the apex of the lower petal are narrow. In *F. occidentalis* the margins at the apex of the lower petal are very broad, while in *F. officinalis*, *F. parviflora* and *F. vaillantii* the margins are so wide as to give the lower petal a spathulate appearance.

3. Fruits

Fruits provide some very useful identification characters (Figure 5). They may be wider than long with an emarginate apex, as in *F. officinalis* subsp. *officinalis*. In *F. occidentalis* the fruits may be as large as 3 × 3 mm, with a rough, tuberculate periderm, and a very marked, strong keel.

One of the most useful diagnostic characters is the presence of a distinct neck to the base of the fresh fruits. This distinct neck is like a ring between the fruits and the pedicel, but it shrivels quite strongly as the fruits dry. It is seen both in *F. capreolata* and *F. purpurea*. In *F. muralis* subsp. *boraei*, and in some other species, the neck is described as being indistinct. The difference between the two kinds of fruits is not always well understood, but when the neck is indistinct the fruits merely narrow to a less wide portion before joining the pedicel. In *F. bastardii* there is no neck at all and the base of the fruits is wider than the tip of the pedicel.

The periderm (fruit coat) may remain smooth as the fruits dry or it may become quite rough. This is not always an easy character to assess and the dry fruits need to be examined with a high magnification lens. The periderm

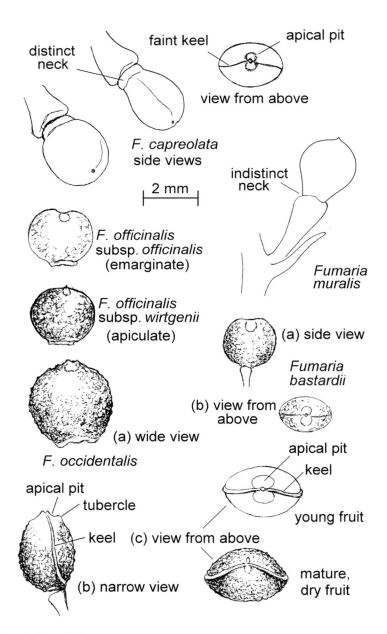

distinct neck

faint keel

apical pit

view from above

F. capreolata side views

2 mm

indistinct neck

Fumaria muralis

F. officinalis subsp. *officinalis* (emarginate)

F. officinalis subsp. *wirtgenii* (apiculate)

(a) side view

Fumaria bastardii

(b) view from above

(a) wide view

F. occidentalis

apical pit

keel

young fruit

apical pit

tubercle

keel (c) view from above

(b) narrow view

mature, dry fruit

Figure 5. *Fumaria* fruits.

of *F. muralis* subsp. *boraei* remains mostly smooth, or at the most faintly rugulose when dry, but *F. bastardii* is readily recognised by a particular combination of rough (or rugose) periderm to the dry fruits with a base that is wider than the tip of the pedicel.

The apex of the fruits can provide other useful features. In a number of species the fruits are rounded-obtuse at the apex, but a slight apiculus may also be present, as in *F. parviflora* var. *parviflora.* A well-defined apiculus may be seen in *F. muralis*, *F. officinalis* subsp. *wirtgenii* and *F. reuteri*. It is even more marked in *F. parviflora* var. *acuminata* where the apex of the fruits is clearly acute. Emarginate fruit apices are rare and these are seen in *F. occidentalis* and *F. officinalis* subsp. *officinalis*.

4. Fruiting Racemes

The angle at which fruits are held on their pedicels can be quite distinctive (Figure 6). In *F. bastardii*, some forms of *F. muralis*, and in *F. officinalis*, the pedicels are erect or erecto-patent. In *F. capreolata* all pedicels are arcuate-recurved, like an inverted U, while in *F. purpurea* and sometimes in *F. muralis* the pedicels are variable, some erecto-patent, some patent, others gently recurved, but never all arcuate-recurved.

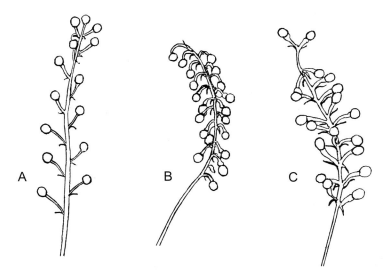

Figure 6. Fruiting racemes of *Fumaria* species. A, *F. bastardii*, pedicels erect to erecto-patent. B, *F. capreolata*, all pedicels arcuate-recurved. C, *F. purpurea*, very variable, from erecto-patent to arcuata-recurved.

In *F. muralis* subsp. *boraei* the flowers may become recurved and hang down like those of *F. purpurea* and the pedicels may be more recurved than usual, but the presence of the smaller, ovate and dentate sepals will indicate its identity.

5. Pedicels, Peduncles, Bracts and Racemes

The proportionate lengths of bracts to pedicels, and racemes to peduncles, are not easy characters to use. In both cases there is much variation. Bracts can be shorter or longer than normal. When *F. officinalis* is growing in adverse conditions, as on a dry wall, the pedicels can be stunted and the bracts appear longer than usual, even longer than the pedicel. The reverse can happen in the case of *F. densiflora* so that the bract can, at times, be shorter than the fruiting pedicel. The bracts can also vary in length on the same raceme, the lowest bracts often being longer than the upper bracts. This happens most frequently in *F. purpurea* where the lowest bracts can be extremely long and sometimes even foliaceus. In a few instances the length of the bracts in relation to the pedicels is strongly indicative of a particular species; for example *F. bastardii* where the bracts are often less than half the length of the pedicel.

In the scandent or climbing fumitories (those that scramble up through hedgebanks and vegetation), the lower peduncles will be longer than usual as the flowering racemes grow towards the light. This happens most frequently in *F. purpurea*, but when this species is growing in more open habitats, as in arable fields, this lengthening of the peduncle does not occur. Where the raceme is much longer than the peduncle such variation is less likely. In *F. densiflora*, *F. officinalis*, *F. parviflora* and *F. vaillantii*, the peduncles can be so short that the racemes may be described as subsessile or they may be sessile. *Fumaria bastardii*, however, requires care in this instance; in an open situation the raceme will be much longer than the peduncle, but where the plants are growing in hedges, the proportion of raceme to peduncle will change and the peduncle will be longer than usual.

In shade the appearance of the pedicels can change. Where normally they are straight, they may become recurved as in *F. muralis*. Contrary to this, in *F. capreolata* where the pedicels are normally recurved, they can become straight.

6. Stigmas

Stigma shapes (Figure 2) are best examined under a microscope. Lay the flower on its side and remove the sepal. Carefully remove the lateral petal, which is easiest starting from the base as the lateral petals are fused at their tips. Sometimes the lower petal needs removing too (again start from the base). The style is long and much thicker than the filaments, and curves upward at the end. The stigma is usually covered with pollen from the anthers.

To loosen and remove pollen from the stigma, brush with a very fine paintbrush soaked in water, and then remove the pollen with a dissecting needle. The stigma is the lobed structure that can then be seen at the top of the style.

Keys to *Fumaria* in Britain and Ireland

The purpose of Key A is to allow the user to name a fumitory to species and/or subspecies level. It is both a dichotomous and an extended key, giving extra information where this may help.

Key B is more detailed. It allows the identification of varieties and forms (after Sell 1998) as well as species and subspecies. These varieties and forms are also considered after the relevant species accounts.

Flower characters are considered to be the most important for identification but fumitories are very variable and are much influenced by the time of year and habitat. The first flowers may be larger than normal and later flowers often smaller and paler or even cleistogamous. Care is therefore needed and in most instances, as has been previously emphasised, both well-formed flowers and dry, mature fruits are needed before a plant can be named with certainty.

KEY A

1a Corollas 9 mm or more (cf. Figure 4); lower petals rarely spathulate;
leaf segments flat.. 2
1b Corollas 5–8(–9) mm; lower petals spathulate;
leaf segments flat or channelled 10

2a Corollas 12–14(–15) mm, lower petals with broad
patent margins; wings of upper petals going through
a stage where they have a white margin;
fruits to 3·0 × 3·0 mm ....*F. occidentalis*
2b Corollas 9–12(–14) mm, lower petals with narrow
patent margins; wings of upper petals never with white
margins; fruits to 2·7 × 2·7 mm 3

3a Flowers numerous, 15–25(–35) in an inflorescence;
sepals large, 4·0–6·5(–7) mm, broader than and often
at least half as long as the corolla; fresh fruits
with distinct neck.. 4
3b Flowers usually few, 9–18(–25) in an inflorescence;
sepals smaller, (2·7–)3–5(–5·5) mm, not broader than corolla,
always less than half as long as the corolla; fruits when fresh
either with indistinct neck or no neck.................................. 6

4a   Fruiting racemes lax; fruiting pedicels erecto-patent
     to recurved; flowers pale to deep purple with darker tips
     to upper and lateral petals; wings of upper petal
     concealing keel.. *F. purpurea*
4b   Fruiting racemes rather rigid; fruiting pedicels
     arcuate-recurved; flowers creamy-white with contrasting
     dark tips to upper and lateral petals; greenish keel
     clearly visible above wings of upper petal 5

5a   Fruits usually small, c. 2 × 2 mm,
     subglobose..*F. capreolata* subsp. *capreolata*
                              (continental form, native in the Channel Islands)
5b   Fruits larger, c. 2·5 × 2·5 mm,
     more rectangular in outline.................*F. capreolata* subsp. *babingtonii*
                                        (endemic to Britain and Ireland)

6a   Racemes always much exceeding peduncles in length;
     sepals more or less entire; corolla 11–13 mm;
     stigma with well-developed central papilla .... *F. reuteri*
6b   Racemes sometimes exceeding peduncles in length;
     sepals dentate (except for *F. muralis* subsp. *neglecta*);
     corolla 9–12(-13) mm; stigma without well-developed central papilla 7

7a   Racemes usually longer than peduncles;
     sepals 2–3·5 × 1·5–2·0 mm, strongly serrate all round;
     corollas 9–11(-12) mm, upper petal usually concolorous;
     fruits rugose when dry, with no neck ....*F. bastardii*
7b   Racemes ± equalling peduncles in length;
     sepals 2·7–5·0 × 1·5–3·0 mm, dentate/serrate or subentire;
     corollas 9–12(–13) mm, upper petal not concolorous;
     fruits often smooth when dry, with indistinct neck 8

8a   Sepals 2·7–3·0 mm, subentire;
     corollas 9–10 mm .... *F. muralis* subsp. *neglecta*
8b   Sepals 3·0–5·0 mm, dentate; corollas 9–13 mm 9

9a   Sepals 3·0–4·0 × 1·5–2·5 mm; corollas 9–11 mm,
      pale pink; fruits (1·75–)2–2·25 × 1·7–2·0 mm,
      smooth when dry ....*F. muralis* subsp. *muralis*
9b   Sepals 3·0–5·0 × 1·5–3·0 mm; corollas 9–12(–13) mm,
      pale to deep rose-pink; fruits 2·25–2·5 × (2·0–)2·25–2·5 mm,
      obscurely rugulose when dry..........................*F. muralis* subsp. *boraei*

10a Sepals conspicuous, 2–3·5 × 1·5–3 mm, pinkish-white,
      nearly orbicular, broader than corolla...............................*F. densiflora*
10b Sepals inconspicuous, 0·5–3·5 × 0·25–1·5 mm,
      narrower than corolla.. 11

11a Sepals 1·2–3·5 × 0·7–1·5 mm; corollas 7–9 mm,
      pale to deep purplish-pink 12
11b Sepals 0·5–0·75(–1·2) × 0·5–0·75 mm, very small;
      corollas 5–6 mm, white or pink.. 13

12a Racemes (10–)20–45(–60)-flowered; sepals (2–)2·5–3·5 × 1–1·5 mm;
      corollas 7–9 mm; lower petal pointed at apex;
      fruits 2·0–2·5 × 3·0 mm, distinctly wider than long,
      apex emarginate..................................... *F. officinalis* subsp. *officinalis*
12b Racemes 5–20(–24)-flowered; sepals 1·5–2·0 × 0·75–1 mm;
      corollas 7–8 mm; lower petal truncate at apex;
      fruits 2–2·25 × 2·25–2·5 mm, not much wider
      than long, ± apiculate ....*F. officinalis* subsp. *wirtgenii*

13a Leaf segments channelled; bracts as long as or longer
      than fruiting pedicels; flowers white, flushing to pink
      as they age; sepals 0·5–0·75(–1·2) × 0·5–0·75 mm...........*F. parviflora*
13b Leaf segments flat; bracts shorter than fruiting pedicels;
      flowers pink; sepals 0·5–0·75(–1) × 0·25–0·5 mm ....*F. vaillantii*

KEY B

1a Corollas 9 mm or more; lower petals not or rarely spathulate;
    leaf segments flat 2
1b Corollas 5–8(–9) mm; lower petals spathulate;
    leaf segments flat or channelled 19

2a Corollas 12–14(–15) mm, lower petals with broad patent margins;
    wings of upper petals going through a stage where they
    have a white margin; fruits to 2·75–3·0 × 2·75–3·0 mm,
    strongly keeled .... *F. occidentalis*
2b Corollas 9–12(–14) mm, lower petals with narrow patent margins;
    wings of upper petals never with a white margin;
    fruits 2·0–2·7 × 2·0–2·7 mm, not strongly keeled 3

3a Flowers numerous, 15–25(–35) in an inflorescence;
    sepals large, 4·0–6·5(–7) mm, broader than and often
    at least half as long as the corolla; fruits when fresh
    with distinct neck 4
3b Flowers usually few, 9–18(–25) in an inflorescence;
    sepals smaller, (2·7–)3–5(–5·5) mm, not broader than
    corolla, always less than half as long as the corolla;
    fruits when fresh either with indistinct neck or no neck 8

4a Fruiting racemes lax; fruiting pedicels erecto-patent to recurved;
    flowers pale to deep purple with darker tips to upper and lateral
    petals; wings of upper petals concealing keel .... *F. purpurea*
4b Fruiting racemes rather rigid; fruiting pedicels arcuate-recurved;
    flowers crimson or creamy-white with contrasting dark tips to
    upper and lateral petals; greenish keel clearly visible above wings
    of upper petals 5

5a Flowers deep crimson .... *F. capreolata* subsp. *capreolata* f. *speciosa*
5b Flowers creamy-white or tinted red or pink 6

6a Fruits c. 2 × 2 mm or smaller, subglobose, apex very obtuse,
    smooth when dry .... *F. capreolata* subsp. *capreolata* f. *capreolata*
6b Fruits c. 2·5 × 2·5 mm, ± rectangular in outline, ± faintly
    rugulose when dry 7

7a Corollas creamy-white, can be flushed red or pink
along dorsal side of upper petal after fertilisation,
fruits more or less rectangular in outline
and truncate at apex. *F. capreolata* subsp. *babingtonii* var. *babingtonii*
(widespread Britain and Ireland)
7b Corollas dusty pink-purple, fruits more
rounded in outline....*F. capreolata* subsp. *babingtonii* var. *devoniensis*
(rare, in North Devon only)

8a Racemes much exceeding the peduncles in length;
sepals entire to sub-entire 9
8b Racemes exceeding the peduncles or ± equal to the peduncle;
sepals dentate to serrate 10

9a Sepals 3–5 mm; corollas 11–13 mm; stigmas with well-developed
central papilla .... *F. reuteri*
9b Sepals 2·7–3·0 mm; corollas 9–10 mm; stigmas without
well-developed central papilla..................... *F. muralis* subsp. *neglecta*

10a Racemes usually exceeding the peduncles;
sepals 2–3·5 mm, strongly serrate; corolla 9–11(-12) mm,
upper petals usually concolorous.. 11
10b Racemes ± equalling peduncles; sepals 2·7–5·5 mm, dentate;
corolla 9–12(–13) mm, upper petals not concolorous 13

11a Upper petals without blackish wings............. *F. bastardii* var. *bastardii*
11b Upper petals with blackish wings.. 12

12a Plants rather dwarf; corollas rather blunt at apex,
fruits c. 2 × 2 mm ....*F. bastardii* var. *gussonei*
(rare)
12b Plant diffuse and straggling; corollas very acute at apex;
fruits c. 2·5 × 2·5 mm .... *F. bastardii* var. *hibernica*
(more frequent than var. *gussonei*)

13a Sepals 3·0–4·0 mm; corollas (8·5–)9–11 mm, pale pink;
fruits c. 2 × 2 mm, smooth when dry.. 14
13b Sepals 3·0–5·5 mm; corollas 9–13 mm, pale to deep rose-pink;
fruits 2–2·5 × 2–2·5 mm, often obscurely rugulose when dry 16

14a Corollas 9–11 mm, lower petals not spathulate
....*F. muralis* subsp. *muralis* var. *muralis*
14b Corollas 8·5–11 mm, lower petals sub-spathulate 15

15a Corollas 8·5–10 mm; sepals 3·5–4·0 × 2·0–2·5 mm
.... *F. muralis* subsp. *muralis* var. *cornubiensis*
15b Corollas 9·0–11 mm, sepals 3·0–3·5 × c. 1·5 mm.............. *F.* × *painteri*

16a Sepals 3·0–4·0 × 1·5–2·7 mm; corollas 9–10 mm, pale pink;
fruits 1·7–2·0 mm × 1·7-2·0 mm, sub-globose to
sub-globose-ovoid ....*F. muralis* subsp. *boraei* var. *britannica*
16b Sepals 4·0–5·0 × 2·0–3·0 mm; corollas 9–12(–13) mm, pale to deep
pink;
fruits 2·5 × 2·0(–2·5) mm 17

17a Fruits 2·5 × 2·5 mm, nearly square in profile ....
....*F. muralis* subsp. *boraei* var. *ambigua*
17b Fruits 2·5 × 2·0 mm, obovate or rounded-obtuse in profile 18

18a Plants slender; pedicels slender; corollas 10–11 mm,
pale-pink; bracts as long as fruiting
pedicels...................................... *F. muralis* subsp. *boraei* var. *gracilis*
18b Plants robust; pedicels stout; corollas 10–12(–13) mm,
pale to deep rose-pink; bracts not as long as fruiting
pedicels.....................................*F. muralis* subsp. *boraei* var. *major*

19a Sepals conspicuous, 2–3·5 × 1·5–3 mm,
nearly orbicular, broader than corolla;
corollas 6–7 mm, short and broad ....*F. densiflora*
19b Sepals inconspicuous, 0·5–3·5 × 0·25–1·5 mm,
narrower than corolla... 20

20a Sepals 1·2–3·5 × 0·7–1·5 mm; corollas (6–)7–9 mm,
pale to deep purplish-pink 21
20b Sepals 0·5–0·75 × 0·5–0·75 mm, very small;
corollas 5–6 mm, white or pink.. 24

21a Racemes (10–)20–45(–60)-flowered; sepals (2–)2·5–3·5 × 1–1·5 mm;
corollas 7–9 mm; lower petals pointed at apex;
fruits 2·0–2·5 × 2·5–3·0 mm, wider than long, apex emarginate 22
21b Racemes (5–)10–20(–24)-flowered; sepals 1·5–2·0 × 0·75–1 mm;
corollas 7–8 mm, lower petal truncate at apex;
fruits 2·0–2·25 × 2·25–2·5 mm, not much wider than long,
± apiculate 23

22a Pedicels robust; corollas 7–9 mm, purplish-pink; fruits
2·0–2·5 × 2·5–3·0 mm.... *F. officinalis* subsp. *officinalis* var. *officinalis*
22b Pedicels slender; corollas 7 mm, pale purplish-pink;
fruits 2·0 × 2·5 mm .... *F. officinalis* subsp. *officinalis* var. *elegans*

23a Leaves ± glaucous; corollas deep pink;
fruits 2·0–2·5 × 2·0–2·5 mm, rounded, often with small
persistent apiculus .... *F. officinalis* subsp. *wirtgenii* var. *wirtgenii*
23b Leaves glaucous; corollas pale pink; fruits 2·0 × 2·5–3·0 mm,
retuse at apex .... *F. officinalis* subsp. *wirtgenii* var. *minor*

24a Leaves very glaucous; leaf segments flat;
sepals 0·5–0·7(–1) × 0·25–0·5 mm; corollas 5–6 mm, pink;
bracts shorter than fruiting pedicels....................................*F. vaillantii*
24b Leaves glaucous; leaf segments channelled; sepals 0·5–0·75(–1·2) ×
0·5–0·75 mm; corollas 5–6 mm, white flushing to pink as they age;
bracts as long as or longer than fruiting pedicels.............................. 25

25a Fruits acute at apex with clear apiculus.... *F. parviflora* var. *acuminata*
25b Fruits rounded or with a beak at apex.. 26

26a Fruits rounded at apex, slight apiculus .... *F. parviflora* var. *parviflora*
26b Fruits with short beak at apex........................... *F. parviflora* var. *symei*

Species accounts

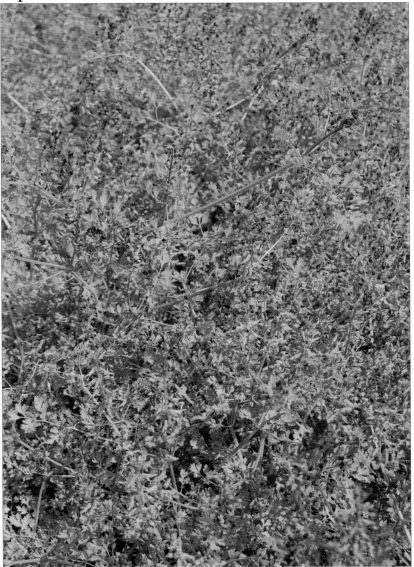

Figure 7. *Fumaria officinalis*, Campbeltown, v.c. 101.

1. *Fumaria capreolata* L.

White Ramping-fumitory

Plant diffuse or climbing by means of cirrhose (coiling) petioles, leaf segments narrowly obovate or cuneiform, flat. **Racemes** (9–)14–25(–35)-flowered, shorter than or equalling the peduncles. **Bracts** a third to half the length of the normally rigidly arcuate-recurved fruiting pedicels. **Sepals** 4–6(–7) × 2–4 mm, sub-entire to dentate, oval to oblong in shape, broader than the corolla, and at times marked with broad green mid-vein. **Corollas** 10–13(–14) mm, laterally compressed, spur broad, apex acute, creamy-white with strongly contrasting dark tips, but often flushed pinkish-red after fertilisation, wings of upper petal narrow and not obscuring the green, humped keel, wings and tips of lateral petals blackish-red, lower petal with narrow, patent margin and green keel. **Fruits** 2–2·25(–2·5) × 2–2·25(–2·5) mm when dry, ± square in outline, periderm remaining smooth when dry or becoming very slightly rugulose towards the indistinct, rather obscure keel, apex obtuse to truncate, apical pits small, with a distinct fleshy neck when fresh; 2n = 64.

Fumaria capreolata is characterised by the dense usually narrow inflorescences with large creamy-white flowers which hang downwards suddenly, and the fruits which have a distinct fleshy neck (Figures 8-14). It has two sub-species, each of which has an infraspecific taxon.

1a. *Fumaria capreolata* subsp. *capreolata*

Bracts usually shorter than fruiting pedicels. **Sepals** 4·0–6·5 × 2–4 mm. **Fruits** c. 2 × 2 mm, variable in size, often smaller than in subsp. *babingtonii*, apex rounded to obtuse, periderm remaining smooth when dry (Figures 9, 10, 14).

This subspecies is very common around the Mediterranean and in southern Europe. It also occurs in the Channel Islands and it is rarely casual elsewhere in Britain (e.g. v.c. 21, 29).

- forma *speciosa* Pugsley is a very distinctive form that is recognised by the rapidity with which the corolla turns bright crimson after fertilisation. It has been recorded from the Channel Islands and occurs sporadically around the Mediterranean.

24

1. *Fumaria capreolata*

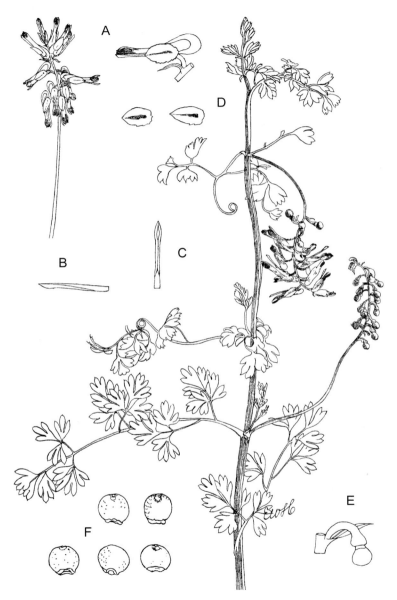

Figure 8. *Fumaria capreolata* (del. E. W. Hunnybun, edited from Moss 1920).
A, flower. B, lower petal, side view. C, lower petal, top view. D, sepals. E, fresh fruit.
F, dry fruits.

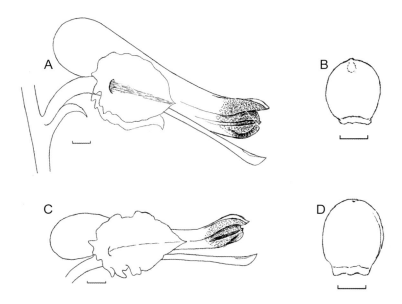

Figure 9. Comparison of *Fumaria capreolata* flowers and fruits. A, B, subsp. *capreolata*. C, D, subsp. *babingtonii*. Scale bar 1 mm.

1b. *Fumaria capreolata* subsp. *babingtonii* (Pugsley) P.D. Sell

Bracts ± equal to the fruiting pedicels. **Sepals** may be slightly longer, to 7 mm, more oblong and sub-entire (as in the Isles of Scilly, see Figure 58), and generally narrower than in subsp. *capreolata*. **Fruits** to 2·5 × 2·5 mm, often larger than in subsp. *capreolata*, more square in outline and becoming faintly rugulose when dry (Figures 9, 10, 14). Endemic to Britain and Ireland (Figure 15).

- var. *devoniensis* Pugsley is a British endemic that is confined to an area around Woolacombe in North Devon (v.c. 4). In this variety the corolla is a dusty pink-purple, the bracts are as long as the less recurved fruiting pedicels and the fruits, to 2·5 × 2·5 mm, are more rounded and become obscurely rugulose when dry. Lidén (1986) listed it under *F. purpurea*, but in var. *devoniensis* the wings of the upper petal do not obscure the keel.

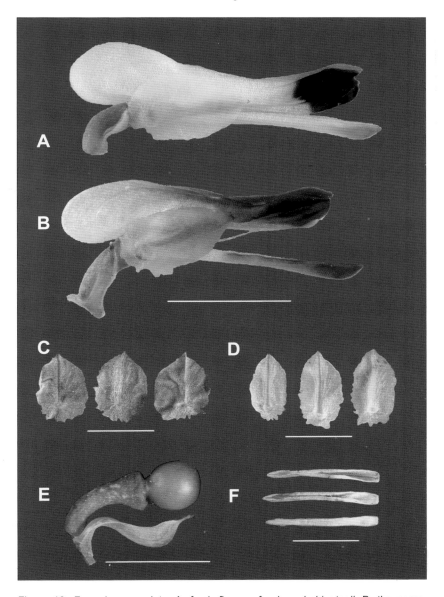

Figure 10. *Fumaria capreolata*. A, fresh flower of subsp. *babingtonii*. B, the same, flushing pink with age (from Gower, v.c. 41). C, subsp. *capreolata* sepals (Sark, v.c. S). D, subsp. *babingtonii* sepals (Campbeltown, v.c. 101). E, subsp. *babingtonii* fruits (Gower, v.c. 41). and F, lower petals (Campbeltown, v.c. 101). Scale bars 5 mm.

Figure 11. *Fumaria capreolata* inflorescence, Caherdaniel, S. Kerry, v.c. H1 (D.T. Holyoak).

Figure 12. Lower stem leaves of *Fumaria capreolata*; Gower, v.c. 41.

Figure 13. *Fumaria capreolata* in fruit (D.T. Holyoak).

Fumaria capreolata scrambles through and over hedgebanks and grows in scrub, on old walls, on coastal cliffs and occasionally on shingle (as on Holy Island). It may also appear in arable and other cultivated fields, on waste ground and in gardens. Often acting as a winter annual, it can come into flower very early in the year, sometimes as early as January in the Isles of Scilly.

A useful summary of the ecology of *F. capreolata* is given in Stewart *et al.* (1994). Its distribution, especially on or near the coast, is relatively stable (Preston *et al.* 2002), although there have been some losses in its inland sites which may only have been casual populations. Its IUCN threat status is of 'Least Concern' in Britain (Cheffings & Farrell 2005) and probably the same in Ireland.

Fumaria capreolata is a Submediterranean – Subatlantic species, distributed through southern and western Europe.

Figure 14a. *Fumaria capreolata* subsp. *capreolata* dried fruits. Corfu.

Figure 14b. *Fumaria capreolata* subsp. *babingtonii* dried fruits. Mayals, v.c. 44.

1. *Fumaria capreolata*

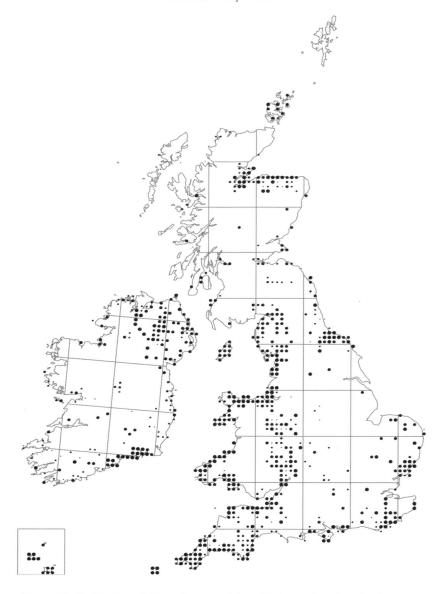

Figure 15. Distribution of *Fumaria capreolata*, with increasing dot size for more recent records.

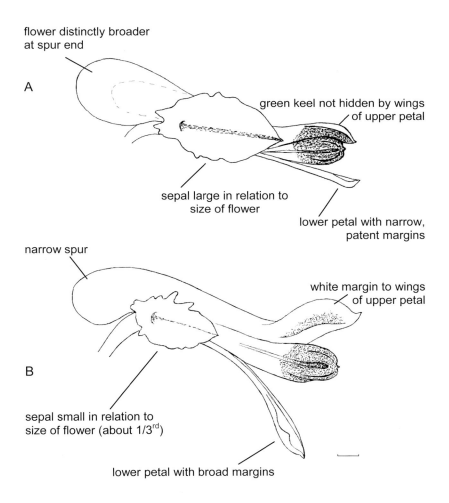

flower distinctly broader
at spur end

A

green keel not hidden by wings
of upper petal

sepal large in relation to
size of flower

lower petal with narrow,
patent margins

narrow spur

white margin to wings
of upper petal

B

sepal small in relation to
size of flower (about 1/3rd)

lower petal with broad margins

Figure 16. Comparison of flowers of A, *Fumaria capreolata* (top) and B, *F. occidentalis*. Scale bar 1 mm.

2. *Fumaria occidentalis* Pugsley

Western Ramping-fumitory

Plant robust, often scandent, readily scrambling through and overtopping hedges. Leaf segments oblong-lanceolate, flat. **Racemes** (8–)12–20(–25)-flowered, as long as or a little longer than the peduncle, somewhat lax. **Bracts** a third to half the length of the fruiting pedicels, which can vary from slightly arcuate to patent, or even erecto-patent. **Sepals** 4–5(–5·5) × 2–3(–3·5) mm, ovate, dentate, especially towards the base, about a third the length of the flower. **Corollas** 12–14(–15) mm, white at first, except for the blackish-red tips to the inner, lateral petals; wings of upper petal soon developing a reddish colouration edged by a broad white margin, the whole flower eventually becoming deeply coloured, pink or pinky-red; lower petal with broad, patent margins. **Fruits** 2·75–3 × 2·75–3 mm, an indistinct neck present when fresh, becoming strongly keeled with a conspicuous tubercle below each broad apical pit, periderm tuberculate-rugose when dry with a dull tint; $2n = 112$.

Fumaria occidentalis is characterised by its large, robust habit, the large white flowers with a white margin to the wing of the upper petal, the broad inflorescences and the fruits that reach 3 × 3 mm, the largest size of all fumitories in Britain (Figures 17-24).

First described by Pugsley (1904), *F. occidentalis* is endemic to Cornwall and the Isles of Scilly (Figures 25, 26). It is listed as Nationally Scarce in Wigginton (1999), this status being based on rarity, but it is now considered, on the basis of threat, to be of 'Least Concern' (Cheffings & Farrell 2005). Nonetheless, all localities should be documented.

Pugsley described it as a 'singularly beautiful plant', hardly to be mistaken for any other species except perhaps *F. capreolata* 'whose aspect it (can) assume to some extent, owing to the pale and recurving flowers'. It is a mistake that can still be made and care has to be taken in the recognition of the differences between the two species (Figure 16).

Pugsley's (1904) original description and his later account in Vol. III of the *Cambridge British Flora* (Pugsley 1920) drew attention to the large flowers with the characteristic white margin to the wings of the upper petal and the large fruits. In the light of recent research and further observation, a greater understanding of the species has become possible. Pugsley had considered it to be related to some of the large-flowered, large-fruited fumitories of the Mediterranean area, such as *F. agraria*. He also considered

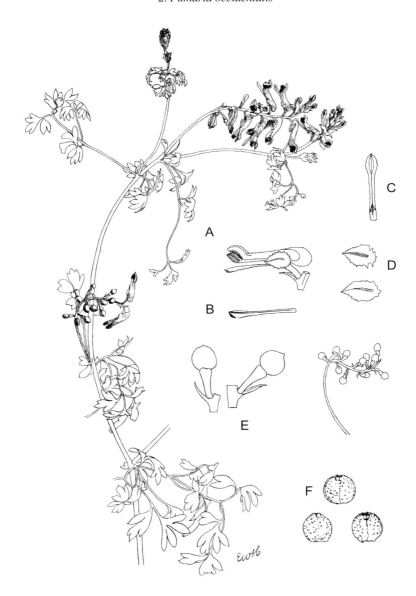

Figure 17. *Fumaria occidentalis* (del. E. W. Hunnybun, edited from Moss 1920). A, flower. B, lower petal, side view. C, lower petal, top view. D, sepals. E, fresh fruits. F, dry fruits.

Figure 18. *Fumaria occidentalis* mass of inflorescences, Lelant, v.c. 1.

the restriction of *F. occidentalis* to the warmest parts of Britain, namely west Cornwall and the Isles of Scilly, to add support to his idea as this was in contrast to the range of the other British endemic *F. purpurea*, which occurs from Cornwall to Orkney. It has been suggested that *F. occidentalis* is an allopolyploid derivative of a cross between *F. capreolata* (2n = 64) and *F. bastardii* (2n = 48), *F. occidentalis* showing some characters that are intermediate between these two possible parents (Daker 1965; Lidén 1986). Wilson *et al.* (1990) provide some experimental support for this hypothesis.

Fumaria occidentalis is found most frequently in disturbed habitats, on waste ground, building sites, newly created banks following road alterations, hedgebanks and in arable fields. An opportunist, it can be quite casual in its occurrence; sudden appearances and equally sudden disappearances are quite typical. This can make it difficult to judge its long-term population trends. When disturbed habitats are plentiful it can show a temporary increase in its distribution, as it did between 1987 and 1999 (Preston *et al.* 2002). When such habitats are few, the populations decrease. At present in Cornwall its numbers seem to be stable. However, it has disappeared from many arable fields on the Isles of Scilly as these have reverted to grass. There are also several Cornish pre-1987 tetrads where it has never been refound. It may be that this plant requires a threat status that is more than of 'Least Concern'. It will be interesting to see if it starts to colonise the new ground, both in v.c. 1 and v.c. 2, that has been created by

2. *Fumaria occidentalis*

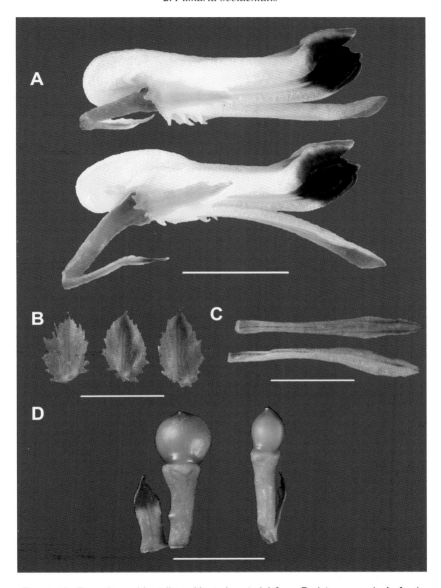

Figure 19. *Fumaria occidentalis*, cultivated material from Padstow, v.c. 1. A, fresh flowers showing white margin to upper petal. B, sepals. C, lower petals. D, fresh fruits (right hand fruit, side view). Scale bars 5 mm.

Figure 20. *Fumaria occidentalis* inflorescence, Mullion, v.c. 1.

Figure 21. Lower stem leaves of *Fumaria occidentalis*; Mullion, v.c. 1.

Figure 22. *Fumaria occidentalis* showing persistent sepals, Mullion, v.c. 1.

the recent road constructions in Cornwall. C.N. French has observed that it does not appear on newly built banks with the first flush of colonising species, but appears either later in the season or in the second year. *Fumaria occidentalis* even seems to have difficulty in spreading as far as East Cornwall, where occurrences are often rather transitory. When it is also considered that this robust plant can still be in flower in December and flowers can be seen as early as January and February, it is strange to think that such a successful species can be so restricted in its distribution.

Figure 23. *Fumaria occidentalis* plants on waste soil, Lelant, v.c. 1.

Figure 24. *Fumaria occidentalis* dried
fruits, Cornwall, v.c. 1.

v.c. 2

Isles of Scilly

v.c. 1

Figure 25. Tetrad distribution of *Fumaria occidentalis* in Cornwall and the Isles of
Scilly.

2. *Fumaria occidentalis*

Figure 26. Distribution of *Fumaria occidentalis*, with increasing dot size for more recent records.

3. *Fumaria bastardii* Boreau

Tall Ramping-fumitory

Plant robust or slender, suberect to diffuse, rarely climbing. Leaf segments oblong to narrowly elliptic, flat. **Racemes** (9–)10–23(–26)-flowered, somewhat lax, usually much longer than the peduncles, rarely almost equalling them. **Bracts** about a third the length of the straight, erect to patent, thickened fruiting pedicels, sometimes longer, pedicels never recurved. **Sepals** 2–3(–3·5) × (1–)1·5–2·0 mm, oval, small, margin strongly dentate (serrate) all round, long-persistent. **Corollas** (8–)9–11(–12) mm, pale or salmon-pink, upper petal concolorous, in some forms the wings are blackish-red like the tips of the lateral, inner petals; lower petal with narrow, patent margins. **Fruits** 2–2·25(–2·5) × 2–2·25(–2·5) mm, rounded to broadly ovate, obscurely keeled, with broad apical pits, base ± wider than tip of pedicel, periderm becoming rugose when dry; 2n = 48.

Fumaria bastardii can be distinguished by the combination of the large salmon-pink flowers with small, strongly-toothed sepals (Figures 27-35). The commonest variety is also unique in having uniformly coloured (concolorous) upper petals. It is divided into three varieties (Sell 1998):

- var. *bastardii*. **Corollas** 10–11(–12) mm, upper petal concolorous; **fruits** c. 2·5 × 2·5 mm, usually subacute at apex. The concolorous upper petal is a character that distinguishes it from all other British large-flowered fumitories (Sell 1989).

- var. *gussonei* (Bioss.) Pugsley. **Corollas** 9–10(–11) mm, upper petal with blackish-red wings; **fruits** 2 × 2 mm. More dwarf in habit than the other two varieties, this variety occurs on the Isles of Scilly and the Channel Islands and also around the Mediterranean.

- var. *hibernica* (Pugsley ex Praeger) Pugsley. **Corollas** 9–11 mm, upper petal with blackish-red wings; **fruits** c. 2·5 × 2·5 mm, larger than those of var. *gussonei*. Endemic to western Britain and Ireland, it is the commonest variety in Ireland.

It is not easy to distinguish the two latter varieties, but perhaps the most easily observed difference is in the size of the fruits, 2·5 × 2·5 mm in var. *hibernica* and only about 2 × 2 mm in var. *gussonei* (Sell 1989, 1998). It is not difficult to separate *F. muralis* from *F. bastardii* var. *bastardii* because of the latter's concolorous upper petal, but the similarity of *F. muralis* subsp. *boraei* var. *ambigua* to *F. bastardii* var. *hibernica* is another matter.

40

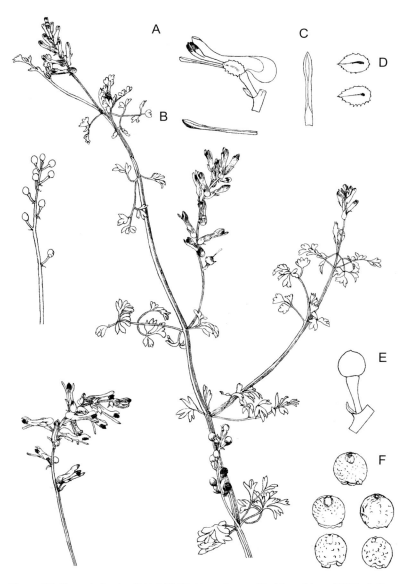

Figure 27. *Fumaria bastardii* (del. E. W. Hunnybun, edited from Moss 1920). A, flower. B, lower petal, side view. C, lower petal, top view. D, sepals. E, fresh fruit. F, dry fruits.

Figure 28. *Fumaria bastardii* on coastal shingle, Killard, v.c. H38.

In both var. *ambigua* and var. *hibernica*, the fruits are nearly square and rugulose (Margetts 1988; Sell 1989). The size of the sepals may provide a helpful clue; in *F. bastardii* the sepals are smaller, no more than 3·5 mm long while in *F. muralis* they can be as much as 5 mm long.

Commonest on cultivated or other disturbed land, *F. bastardii* can be found in gardens, bulb fields and arable fields, on earthy banks and in hedges, along road verges, in waste places and sometimes at the base of walls. It can, at times, also be found by coastal paths and on sea cliffs, but it is most typical of spring-sown crops. *Fumaria bastardii* is a self-compatible species that sets seed freely (Stewart *et al.* 1994). It also produces cleistogamous flowers very readily when habitat conditions are adverse (Lidén 1986).

Fumaria bastardii is moderately frequent in Britain, Ireland and the Channel Islands (Figure 36). Its distribution in Britain is principally western being found from the Isles of Scilly to Orkney. Most of the recent records for Ireland are easterly and in Scotland it may be found in the Scottish Borders and further north-east as well as along the west coast and in the Hebrides.

It is a Mediterranean-Atlantic species that is widely naturalised in other parts of the world. Its IUCN threat status is of 'Least Concern' in Britain (Cheffings & Farrell 2005) and probably the same in Ireland.

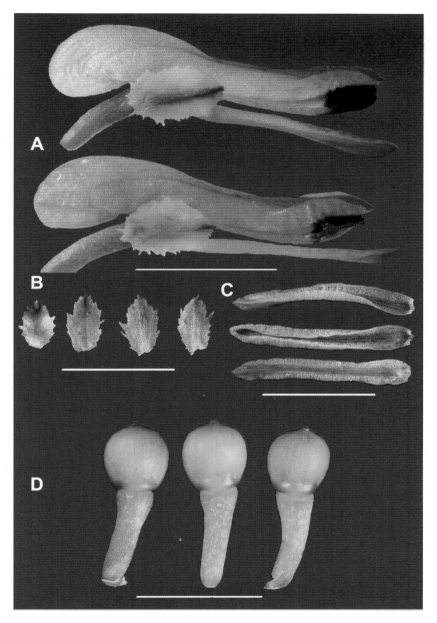

Figure 29. *Fumaria bastardii*, Gower, v.c. 41. A, fresh flowers. B, sepals. C, lower petals. D, fresh fruits. Scale bars 5 mm.

Figure 30. *Fumaria bastardii* leaves.

Figure 31. *Fumaria bastardii* inflorescence and leaves, Pennard, v.c. 41.

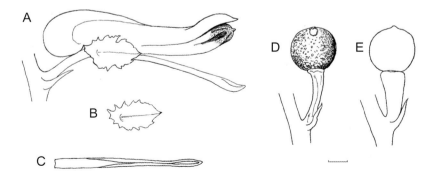

Figure 32. *Fumaria bastardii.* A, flower. B, sepals. C, lower petal. D, dry fruit. E, fresh fruit. Scale bar 1 mm.

Figure 33. *Fumaria bastardii* plants on waste soil, Lelant, v.c. 1.

Figure 34. *Fumaria bastardii* dried fruits, Gower, v.c. 41.

Figure 35. *Fumaria bastardii*, Gower, v.c. 41.

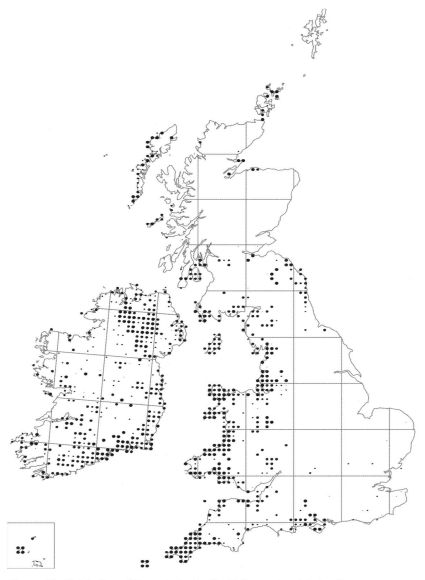

Figure 36. Distribution of *Fumaria bastardii* with increasing dot size for more recent records.

4. *Fumaria reuteri* Boiss

Martin's Ramping-fumitory

Plant robust, branched from base, low-growing, rarely climbing. Leaf segments linear-obovate, oblong or cuneiform, flat. **Racemes** 8–20(–25)-flowered, long and lax, much longer than the very short peduncles. **Bracts** half to two thirds length of fruiting pedicels. Pedicels become arcuate or recurved when flowers reach anthesis, then in fruiting stage pedicels become patent. **Sepals** 3–5 × (1·5–)2–2·25(–3) mm, oval, subentire, sometimes slightly toothed at base, narrower than the corolla tube. **Corollas** (10–)11–13(–14) mm, bright rose-pink, wings of upper petal and tips of lateral petals blackish-red, lower petal with narrow, patent margins. Stigma with a large central, apical appendage between the two lateral ones. **Fruits** 2·2–2·7 × 2·0–2·5 mm , ± ovate or subrotund, obscurely keeled, apical pits distinct, periderm mostly smooth when dry; 2n = 48.

Fumaria reuteri is characterised by the combination of large (11–13 mm), recurved, rose-pink flowers with strong blackish-red tips and almost entire sepals that are never more than 5 mm long (Figures 37-43). The unique stigma with a large central appendage between two lateral lobes is also diagnostic, but note that the actual size of the central appendage will vary a little (Figure 40).

The other large-flowered species differ as follows: *F. capreolata* has crowded inflorescences with creamy-white flowers on pedicels that are eventually strongly arcuate-recurved; *F. purpurea* has larger, oblong, subentire to weakly toothed sepals (to 6·5 mm) and light to deeper purple flowers; *F. bastardii* has smaller (to 3·5 mm), strongly-toothed sepals; and *F. muralis* has ovate, mostly toothed sepals, c. 4–5 mm long. *Fumaria reuteri* is distinguished from *F. muralis* subsp. *neglecta* only in its large corolla and sepals, and the stigma with a large central appendage.

Fumaria reuteri is a western European endemic. Lidén (1986) regards it as being a very variable species with many regional and ecotypic forms that are 'strongly modified by shade in floral characteristics'. Plants in Britain are somewhat distinct from the *F. reuteri* of Spain and Portugal, British material having broader leaf segments, more flowers to the raceme (often 18–24), larger, more showy corollas (sometimes 13–14 mm), and fruits that are more subrotund with larger, though shallow apical pits. However, British *F. reuteri* and Iberian *F. reuteri* also have certain characters in common, namely racemes much longer than the peduncle, sepals subentire and stigma with central, apical papilla. British plants were first named

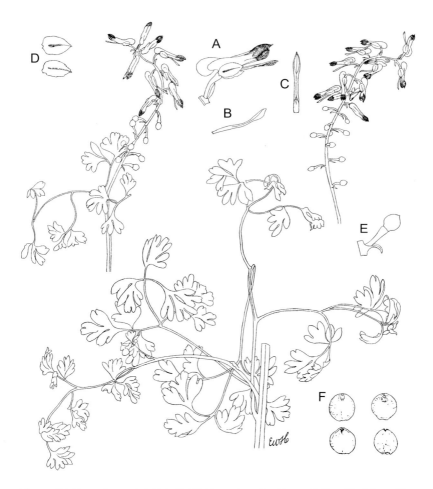

Figure 37. *Fumaria reuteri* (del. E. W. Hunnybun (as *F. martinii*), edited from Moss 1920). A, flower. B, lower petal, side view. C, lower petal, top view. D, sepals. E, fresh fruit. F, dry fruits.

F. paradoxa Pugsley (Pugsley 1912); then *F. martinii* Clavaud (Pugsley 1920); and later *F. reuteri* subsp. *martinii* (Clavaud) A. Soler (Soler 1983). The most recent change was made in 1986 when Magnus Lidén grouped *F. martinii* and *F. reuteri* under the latter name (Lidén 1986). *Fumaria reuteri* would seem, as far as is known at present, to be the best name for British material, as *F. reuteri* of Spain and Portugal has proved so variable,

Figure 38. *Fumaria reuteri* plants, Lake Allotments, v.c. 10.

with forms not only approaching *F. martinii* but even sometimes showing transition states to *F. muralis* (Castroviejo *et al.* 1986), so that it seems difficult to maintain a species separation for the plants, and perhaps they are 'not even subspecifically distinct' (Stace 1997). P.D. Sell, however, considers *F. reuteri* and *F. martinii* to be distinct species.

In Britain *F. reuteri* is a plant of disturbed ground, growing on arable and horticultural land, including allotments. In Cornwall it has also appeared on hedgebanks next to allotments and arable fields. Until 1993 it persisted in small numbers in the allotment garden at Pulla Cross in Cornwall, where it also occurred in potato fields, but as the fields reverted to grass and the allotment garden became neglected the fumitory disappeared. As seed can last for some time in the seedbank, repeat visits to the area are being carried out in case the plant appears once more. It can germinate both amongst spring and summer-sown crops at Lake on the Isle of Wight, and may still be in flower there in October (Wilson 1997).

Fumaria reuteri is sometimes regarded as a neophyte (introduced to Britain after 1500). It was first recorded in Gilly Tresamble (Pulla Cross) in Cornwall (v.c. 1) in 1904, and was last recorded there in 1993. In 1963 it was found on the Isle of Wight (v.c. 10) where it has been maintained with care and good populations still survive (Pope *et al.* 2003). It has recently been recorded in a garden at Campbeltown, Kintyre (v.c. 101) (Teesdale 2008). There are also historical records for Devon, Dorset, Somerset, Surrey, Sussex and Guernsey but it has not been recorded in Ireland (Figure 44).

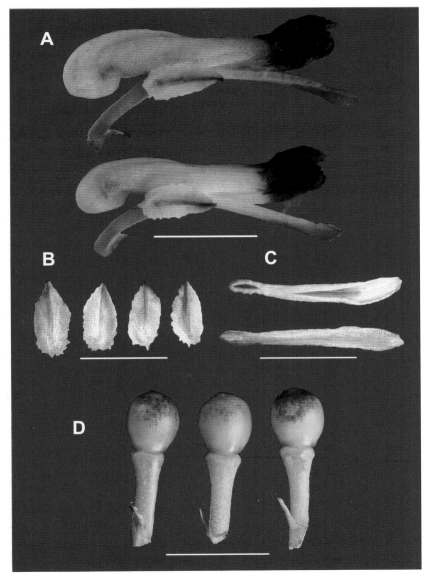

Figure 39. *Fumaria reuteri*, Lake Allotments, v.c. 10. A, fresh flowers. B, sepals. C, lower petals. D, fresh fruits. Scale bars 5 mm.

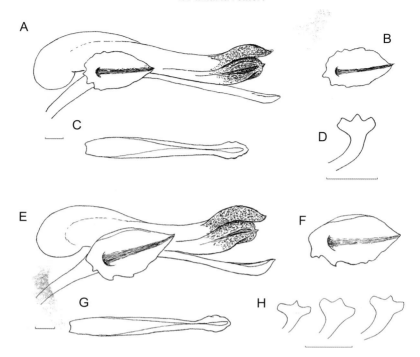

Figure 40. *Fumaria reuteri*. Above, Lake Allotments, v.c. 10. A, flower. B, sepal. C, lower petal. D, stigma. Below, Campbeltown, v.c. 101. E, flower. F, sepal. G, lower petal. H, variation in stigmas. Scale bar 1 mm.

Figure 41. Lower stem leaves of *F. reuteri*; Campbeltown, v.c. 101.

Fumaria reuteri is evidently rare and seriously threatened in Britain (Wigginton 1999) and has been the subject of a 'Species Recovery' report by Wilson (1997) who noted: '*Fumaria reuteri* has been recorded in several sites in southern and south-west England during the 20th Century, and it may still persist in some of these. It may also have been overlooked in others due to its similarity to other *Fumaria* species. All old sites should be surveyed and botanists should be encouraged to examine populations of other large-flowered *Fumaria* species to see whether *F. reuteri* occurs elsewhere'.

At present *F. reuteri* is placed on the 'Waiting List' in the latest Red Data List (Cheffings & Farrell 2005) on the basis that it may either be an archaeophyte or a neophyte. However, it is still protected under Schedule 8 of the Wildlife & Countryside Act 1981, as amended.

Fumaria reuteri is an Oceanic Southern-temperate species occurring in Britain, the Channel Islands, north-west and west-central France, Spain and Portugal. It is naturalised in North America.

Figure 42. *Fumaria reuteri*, dried fruits, Lake Allotments, v.c. 10.

Figure 43. *Fumaria reuteri* inflorescence, Campbeltown, v.c. 101.

4. *Fumaria reuteri*

Figure 44. Distribution of *F. reuteri*, with increasing dot size for more recent records.

5. *Fumaria muralis* Sonder ex W.D.J. Koch

Common Ramping-fumitory

Plant with a dense, well-branched manner of growth, sometimes lax in appearance, rarely climbing. Leaf segments oblong, lanceolate or cuneiform, flat. **Racemes** 8–15(–20)-flowered, lax, equalling or at times exceeding the peduncles. **Bracts** about half as long to nearly as long as the fruiting pedicels that are mostly straight and erecto-patent, but at times flexuous and recurved. **Sepals** 2·7–5·0 × 1·5–3·0 mm, ovate to oval (never oblong), dentate or subentire. **Corollas** (8–)9–12(–13) mm, pale to deep rose-pink, wings of upper petal and tips of lateral petals blackish-red, lower petal narrow with narrow patent margins, only rarely sub-spathulate. **Fruits** c. 2–2·5 × 2–2·5 mm, rounded to square, base usually narrower than apex of pedicel, neck indistinct, apical pits small; fruit wall remaining smooth or becoming finely rugulose when dry; 2n = 48.

Fumaria muralis is a very variable taxon but it can be recognised by the combination of the pale to deep rose-pink flower colour, the blackish-red tips to the upper and lateral petals, the ovate, often toothed sepals that are rarely more than 5 mm long, and the rather smooth fruits with indistinct neck (Figures 45-49).

Fumaria muralis grows on hedgebanks, in gardens, on waste land, at field edges, on allotment and in arable fields amongst a range of crops from bulbs to cereals. It is one of the most frequent fumitories in Britain, Ireland and the Channel Islands, especially in western areas. Because of the difficulties of identification its distribution is usually mapped as *F. muralis* without separating the three subspecies.

In some accounts of the fumitories *F. muralis* is divided into three subspecies – subsp. *muralis*, subsp. *boraei* and subsp. *neglecta* (Pugsley 1920; Sell 1998). *Fumaria muralis*, however, shows an immense range of variation, greater than in any other British fumitory, with the largest number of infraspecific taxa. The complete list of 'varietal' names allocated to this species is very extensive, especially in the older literature (Pugsley 1912, 1920). Sell (1989) stated 'to write a composite description of all the forms of *F. muralis* and to distinguish it from all other species seems to be impossible'. The following descriptions summarise what is known at present, but it is clear that *F. muralis* requires further study.

5. *Fumaria muralis*

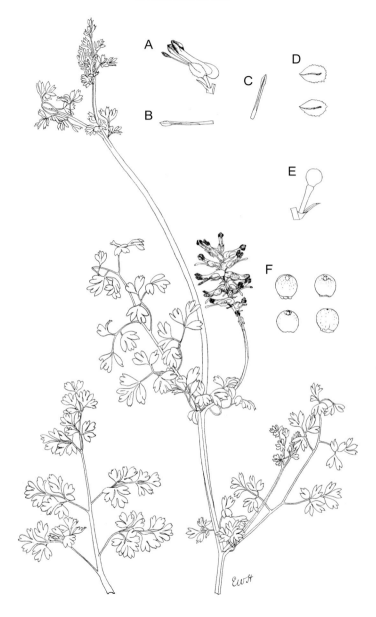

Figure 45. *Fumaria muralis* (del. E. W. Hunnybun, edited from Moss 1920). A, flower. B, lower petal, side view. C, lower petal, top view. D, sepals. E, fresh fruit. F, dry fruits.

Figure 46. *Fumaria muralis* in barley field near Shrewsbury, v.c. 40 (A. Lockton).

5a. *Fumaria muralis* subsp. *muralis*

Subsp. *muralis* may be distinguished by smaller dentate sepals, 3–4 × 1·5–2·5 mm, smaller corollas, 9–11 mm, and small fruits, c. 2 × 2 mm (Sell 1998).

Subsp. *muralis* has been recorded from a very few scattered locations in England, where it has probably been introduced, but there have been no recent records (Perring & Sell 1968). It has been divided into two varieties, but there have been no records for them for some time. Several sources have therefore been used to compile the following descriptions:

- var. *muralis*. Slender. **Racemes** few-flowered, the racemes ± equalling the peduncles. **Bracts** shorter than the fruiting pedicels. **Sepals** 3·0–4·0 × 1·5–2·7 mm, dentate. **Corollas** 9–11 mm, pale-pink with blackish-red wings to upper petal and dark tips to lateral petals, lower petal with narrow margins. **Fruits** 2–2·25 × 2 mm, ovoid, sometimes apiculate, periderm remaining smooth when dry. Scattered through southern

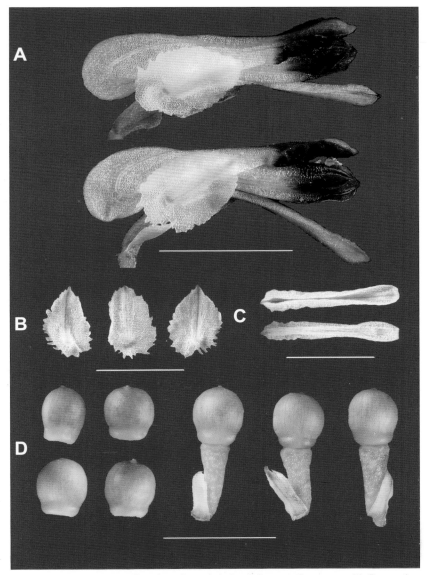

Figure 47. *Fumaria muralis* subsp. *boraei*. A, fresh flowers, Gower v.c. 41. B, sepals, C, lower petals and D, fresh fruits, Westward Ho, v.c. 4. Scale bars 5 mm.

Figure 48. *Fumaria muralis* subsp. *boraei* inflorescence, Westward Ho, v.c. 4.

Britain, but likely to be rare (Sell 1998). The most recent records were made in 1939 for Devon (both v.c. 3 and v.c. 4) by H.W. Pugsley.

- var. *cornubiensis* Pugsley. Slender. **Sepals** 3·0–4·0 × 1·5–2·7 mm, nearly entire. **Corollas** 8·5–10 mm, pale-pink, broad wings to the upper petal, lower petal sub-spathulate with broad, patent margins. **Fruits** c. 2 × 2 mm. An endemic, first recorded from Tregony in East Cornwall (v.c. 2) in 1922 by Miss E.S. Todd and described by H.W. Pugsley (Pugsley 1924; Thurston & Vigurs 1925). Rare and possibly now extinct (Sell 1998), other records for Cornwall have not been confirmed (Margetts & Spurgin 1991).

5b. *Fumaria muralis* subsp. *boraei* (Jord.) Pugsley

Plant usually robust. **Racemes** 8–15(–20)-flowered, shorter than or equalling the peduncles. **Bracts** mostly half as long as the fruiting pedicels which are usually erecto-patent but can be flexuous or recurved. **Sepals** 3–5·0 × 3·0(–3·5) mm, ovate and dentate, a very characteristic shape. **Corollas** 9–13 mm, but less in adverse conditions, very pale pink to deep rosy-red with blackish-red wings to upper petal and blackish-red tips to lateral petals, lower petal narrow with narrow patent margins. **Fruits** 2·0–2·5 × 1·7–2·5 mm, very variable in size, but mostly 2·5 × 2·0 mm, base narrower than apex of pedicel, rounded to square, neck indistinct, periderm remaining smooth or becoming faintly rugulose when dry, apical pits slightly larger than in subsp. *muralis*.

Subsp. *boraei* is the most widespread of the three subspecies of *F. muralis* and is, with *F. bastardii*, one of the two most common large-flowered (over 9 mm) fumitories of western Britain and Ireland (Sell 1989). When the pedicels become flexuous and recurved so that the flowers are deflexed, *F. muralis* subsp. *boraei* can be confused with *F. purpurea*, but the ovate sepal shape and the fruits with their indistinct neck will allow identification.

At present four varieties of *F. muralis* subsp. *boraei* may be recognised (Sell 1998): var. *ambigua*, var. *gracilis*, var. *britannica* and var. *major*. These varieties are rarely recorded, perhaps because three of them, *ambigua*, *britannica* and *gracilis*, are all pale-coloured and there is a tendency for poorly-grown specimens of *F. muralis* subsp. *boraei* also to be pale-coloured. The four varieties have been distinguished as follows.

- var. *ambigua* Pugsley. **Sepals** 4·0–5·0 × 2·0–3·5 mm, rather narrow. **Corollas** rarely more than 11 mm long, pale pink. **Fruits** 2·5 × 2·5 mm, ± square in outline, scarcely narrowed below, slightly rugulose when dry. There are no recent records for this variety though Pugsley (1920) stated that it can be found in North Devon, Somerset and Sussex and perhaps elsewhere in Britain as well as in Wexford in Ireland. It was recorded from Culdrose, just north of the Lizard, in Cornwall (v.c. 1) in 1984, confirmed by P.D. Sell (Margetts 1988).

- var. *gracilis* Pugsley. Slender. **Bracts** as long as fruiting pedicels, a distinguishing character in relation to the other varieties (Sell 1989), pedicels variable, erecto-patent, divaricate, flexuous or even recurved. **Sepals** 4·0–5·0 × 2·0–3·0 mm, broad. **Corollas** 10-11 mm, quite large, but pale pink. **Fruits** 2·5 × 2·0 mm, similar to those of var. *major*. Pugsley (1920) recorded this variety from Cornwall, Hampshire, Surrey, Pembrokeshire and Cardiganshire. There are recent records for Cardiganshire (v.c. 46) and one for Devon (v.c. 3).

- var. *britannica* Pugsley. Slender, diffuse or climbing. **Sepals** 3·0–4·0 × 2–2·7 mm, small, acute. **Corollas** 9–10 mm, small, pale-pink. **Fruits** 1·7–2·0 × 1·7–2·0 mm, small and rarely exceeding 2·0 mm. A distinctive variety, Pugsley (1920) considered this variety to be quite widespread and it may be that some of the apparently poor-growing forms of *F. muralis* subsp. *boraei* are referable to it. There are a few more recent records for the variety, one of these being from The Lizard in Cornwall (v.c. 1), in an old quarry near Tregaddra in 1984, confirmed by P.D. Sell (Margetts 1988).

- var. *major* (Boreau) P.D. Sell. Robust. **Bracts** shorter than the normally straight, erecto-patent pedicels. **Sepals** 4·0–5·0 × 2·5–3·0 mm or even larger and wider. **Corollas** 10–12(–13) mm, larger than those of the other varieties, deep pink to rose-red in colour, sometimes even richer (forma *rubens* Pugsley). **Fruits** 2·5 × 2·0–2·25 mm, not as large or square as in var. *ambigua*, base usually narrower than apex of pedicel, neck indistinct. Formerly known as var. *typica* (Pugsley 1920), or var. *boraei* or var. *major* Koch, this is 'the largest and most handsome of the four varieties of this fumitory' (Sell 1989). Pugsley (1920) stated that 'this is the commonest variety of the subspecies, occurring throughout both Britain and Ireland'. There are at present, however, few recent records for this variety. It was seen in the Isles of Scilly in 1982, 2007 and 2008 and in Cornwall in a hedge near Portloe (v.c. 2) in 1989. In 1974 it was also recorded in North Devon. A very strong, robust and extensive growth of a very brightly coloured *F. muralis* subsp. *boraei* is likely to be this variety.

5c. *Fumaria muralis* subsp. *neglecta* Pugsley

Plant robust. **Racemes** 8–20-flowered, the racemes longer than the peduncles. **Bracts** about half as long as the suberect fruiting pedicels that are never recurved. **Sepals** 2·7–3·0 × 1·5–2·0 mm, sub-entire, rather persistent. **Corollas** 9–10 mm, lower petal not spathulate. **Fruits** mostly 2 × 2 mm, rarely slightly over 2 mm, almost truncate and faintly rugulose when dry.

Endemic, *F. muralis* subsp. *neglecta* was first found in a cultivated field at Gilly Tresamble near Penryn in Cornwall (v.c. 1) in 1907. Other records have been made in Cornwall but the plant has not been seen for years and may well be extinct (Sell 1998). The record for Port Quin in East Cornwall (v.c. 2) was not confirmed (Margetts & Spurgin 1991).

Fumaria muralis is an Oceanic Southern-temperate species of Western Europe (Preston *et al*. 2002), but it is also widely naturalised outside its native range. The IUCN Threat Status is 'Least Concern' in Britain (Cheffings & Farrell 2005) and probably the same in Ireland.

Figure 49a. *Fumaria muralis* subsp. *boraei* lower stem leaves, Gower, v.c. 41.

Figure 49b. *Fumaria muralis* subsp. *boraei* dried fruits, Newport, v.c. 45.

Figure 50. Distribution of *F. muralis* subsp. *boraei*, with increasing dot size for more recent records.

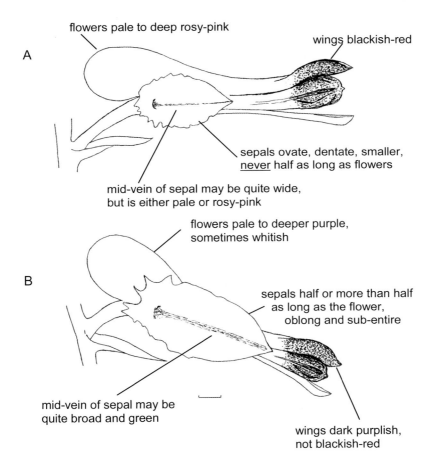

Figure 51. Comparison of *Fumaria muralis* subsp. *boraei* and *F. purpurea* flowers. A, *F. muralis* subsp. *boraei*. B, *F. purpurea*. Scale bar 1 mm.

6. *Fumaria purpurea* Pugsley

Purple Ramping-fumitory

Plant robust, the plants may be diffuse but in its hedge habitat it is scandent, readily growing through and over the associated vegetation. Leaf segments linear to oblong, flat. **Racemes** (11–)15–24(–28)-flowered, long and lax, nearly equalling the peduncles in length. **Bracts** nearly as long as the fruiting pedicels, the lower bracts often much longer and sometimes foliaceous. **Sepals** 4·5–6·5 × 2–3 mm, oblong, subentire, usually dentate only at the base, broader than and at least half as long as the corolla tube, sometimes with a broad green band down the mid-line on the outer surface. **Corollas** 10–13 mm, pale purplish-pink or purple, even paler in the young flower or later in the season, tips of the lateral petals and wings of the upper petal blackish-purple, wings do not quite reach apex of flower, but hide the keel, lower petal with rather narrow patent margins. **Fruits** c. 2·5 × 2·5 mm borne on pedicels that can be patent, recurved or divaricate, the fruits squarish-truncate, obscurely keeled, with broad, apical pits and a distinct neck at the base when fresh, the neck being narrower than the dilated tip of the pedicel, periderm faintly rugulose when dry; 2n = 80.

Fumaria purpurea in its typical form is characterised by the large, recurved, purplish flowers, fruits when fresh with a distinct neck and the large, oblong sepals which are clearly visible even on inflorescences with paler flowers later in the season (Figures 52-56). The occasional occurrence of foliaceous bracts is unique to this species.

Pugsley first named this fumitory in 1902, and described two forms. The common form he called var. *longisepala*, with sepals very oblong and reaching 6·5 mm, which he recorded from Cornwall to Orkney and Ireland. A rarer form with shorter, broader sepals (4·5–5·0 × 2–3 mm) was distinguished as var. *brevisepala* Pugsley and was listed from Cornwall, Shropshire, Caernarvonshire and Ireland. Neither of these varieties is listed by Lidén (1986) or by Sell (1998) and Pugsley himself admitted that his var. *brevisepala* could be confused with *F. muralis* subsp. *boraei*.

In his monograph, Lidén (1986) places *F. purpurea* after the *F. reuteri*/ *F. muralis* group and not with *F. capreolata*. Although *F. purpurea* and *F. capreolata* are similar (large sepals and recurved fruiting pedicels), he rejects *F. capreolata* (2n = 64) as one of the parents of *F. purpurea* (2n = 80) on both chemical (chromatograms) and cytological (chromosomal) grounds, *F. purpurea* having truncate fruits, pollen with many apertures,

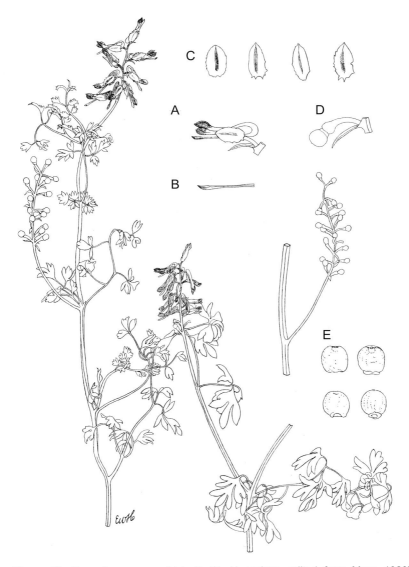

Figure 52. *Fumaria purpurea* (del. E. W. Hunnybun, edited from Moss 1920). A, flower. B, lower petal, side view. C, sepals. D, fresh fruit. E, dry fruits.

Figure 53. *Fumaria purpurea* plant by wall in garden; Cardiff, v.c. 41.

and a weak 'coptisine' spot and traces of 'rutoside' on chromatograms. He states that *F. muralis* subsp. *boraei* (2n = 48) is 'almost certainly' one parent (the flowers and habitat being very similar to those of *F. purpurea*) and suggests that *F. officinalis* (2n = 32) is the second parent (48 + 32 = 80). Coptisine is characteristic of the Capreolatae, including *F. purpurea*, and rutoside and pollen with many apertures is characteristic of the section *Fumaria*, which includes *F. officinalis*. Daker (1964) and P.D. Sell do not take this view and place *F. purpurea* next to *F. capreolata* as the two are similar morphologically.

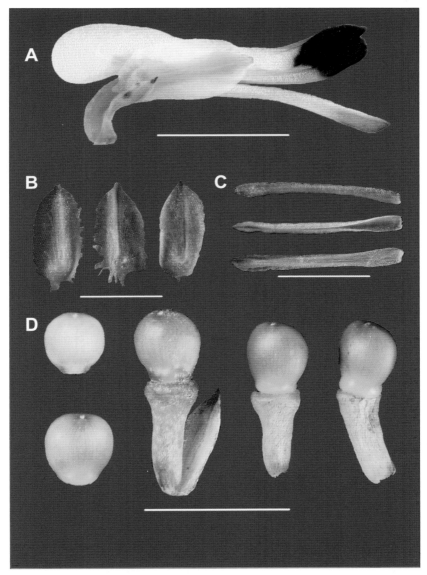

Figure 54. *Fumaria purpurea*, cultivated Cardiff from Orkney material. A, fresh flower. B, sepals. C, lower petals. D, fresh fruits. Scale bars 5 mm.

Figure 55a. *Fumaria purpurea*
inflorescence, Lelant, v.c. 1.

Figure 55b. *Fumaria purpurea*
inflorescence, cultivated, Cardiff.

From a habitat point of view, *F. purpurea* is a most interesting plant. It used to be found in the bulb fields on the Isles of Scilly but has not been seen for some time, perhaps because so many of these fields have reverted to grass. However, it has been found again on Guernsey in the Channel Islands, one of the sites being a sunny, well-drained bank. Elsewhere it has been recorded from waste and disturbed ground, gardens, arable fields, hedgebanks and walls and coastal localities. There is a definite tendency for arable fields to be the most frequent habitat as one goes further north in Britain (Lockton 2003). It is also said to occur on disturbed habitats opened up by summer drought (Wilson 2002).

In parts of Scotland, especially in Orkney (v.c. 111), *F. purpurea* occurs in set-aside areas and gardens as well as arable fields. In the latter habitat it grows with such crops as turnips, oil-seed rape and barley and analysis of the plant associates in Orcadian fields has indicated that *F. purpurea* is found mainly in the NVC type OV4 *Chrysanthemum segetum – Spergula arvensis* community (Crossley 2005; Rodwell 2000). In East Lothian (v.c. 82) where plants grow all through the winter if conditions are suitable, the species can be found on earth dumps associated with building operations, even in areas regularly treated with weed-killer.

In marked contrast to the above, *F. purpurea* becomes extremely rare in arable fields in Cornwall, where the usual habitat is roadside hedgebank or Cornish hedge (earth-core wall), especially those along Cornwall's north coast. There are no records for the species in arable fields in Devon.

Flowering times also vary. In the Scottish Borders *F. purpurea* is usually late-flowering and is 'at its best in September to October' (Braithwaite 2000). In cultivation in Cardiff, it behaves as a winter, spring or summer annual, the former producing the largest plants, sometimes scrambling to 2 m or more tall. In Cornwall there are records for *F. purpurea* in flower for every month from March to October.

Fumaria purpurea is not a widespread species and its distribution seems to be mainly down the west of England and in the east of Scotland and Ireland. It is interesting to note that it used to be quite common on the Welsh Marches but has disappeared from here, and instead has become more restricted to coastal locations. Apart from a few records for the Channel Isles, it has not been recorded outside Britain and Ireland.

Its IUCN threat status is 'Least Concern' in Britain (Cheffings & Farrell 2005) but it has a Biodiversity Action Plan. In Ireland it is probably 'Vulnerable' but it has not been well-recorded in recent years.

Figure 56a. *Fumaria purpurea*, lower stem leaves.

Figure 56b. *Fumaria purpurea*, dried fruits, cultivated, Cardiff.

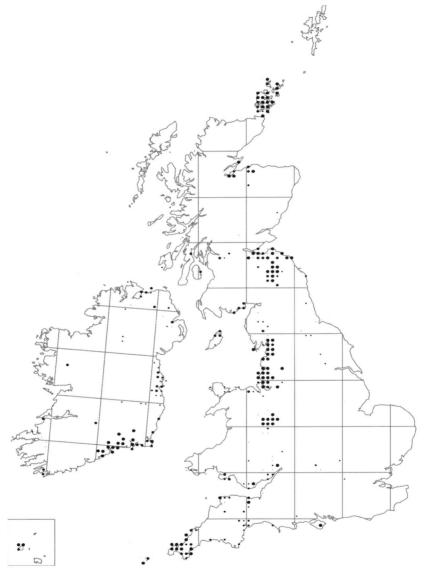

Figure 57. Distribution of *Fumaria purpurea*, with increasing dot size for more recent records.

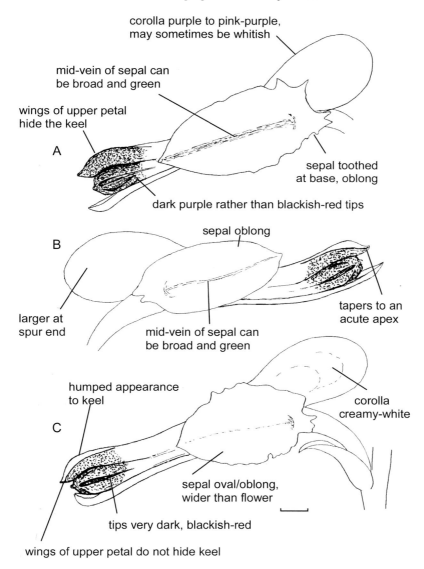

corolla purple to pink-purple,
may sometimes be whitish

mid-vein of sepal can
be broad and green

wings of upper petal
hide the keel

A

sepal toothed
at base, oblong

dark purple rather than blackish-red tips

sepal oblong

B

larger at
spur end

tapers to an
acute apex

mid-vein of sepal can
be broad and green

humped appearance
to keel

corolla
creamy-white

C

sepal oval/oblong,
wider than flower

tips very dark, blackish-red

wings of upper petal do not hide keel

Figure 58. Comparison of *F. purpurea* and *F. capreolata* flowers. A, *F. purpurea*. B, *F. capreolata* subsp. *babingtonii* (a form on the Isles of Scilly). C, *F. capreolata* subsp. *babingtonii*, Penzance, v.c. 1. Scale bar 1 mm.

7. *Fumaria officinalis* L.

Common Fumitory

Plant erect to diffuse, often glaucous, branched extensively from the base. Leaf segments very narrow, 1–2 mm wide, flat. **Racemes** (9–)10–45(–60)-flowered, shortly-stalked, dense. **Bracts** half as long or sometimes equalling the erecto-patent to patent, rigid fruiting pedicels. **Sepals** 1·5–3·5 × 0·7–1·5 mm, often irregularly dentate, rarely subentire, small, variable in shape from oval to lanceolate. **Corollas** (6–)7–8(–9) mm, purplish-pink, often deeply so, wings of upper petal and tips of lateral petals blackish-red, upper petal subspathulate to spathulate, lower petal spathulate with wide, patent margins. **Fruits** 2 × 2·5–3·0 mm, usually broader than long, apical pits shallow, apex shortly apiculate, truncate or emarginate, slight neck, periderm rugose when dry.

Fumaria officinalis is characterised by the moderate-sized flowers (mostly 7-9 mm long), the markedly spathulate lower petal, the small, often lanceolate sepals and the fruits often clearly wider than long (Figures 7, 59-68). Fruits are broader than long in all variants of *F. officinalis* (Sell 1985).

A number of infraspecific taxa have been described (Pugsley 1912, 1920; Lidén 1986; Sell 1985, 1998; Lidén 2002). Two can be recognised in Britain and Ireland:

7a. *Fumaria officinalis* subsp. *officinalis*

Racemes 10–53(–60)-flowered, commonly more than 20-flowered. **Sepals** (2–)2·5–3·5 × 1–1·5 mm, characteristically 2 mm or more in length, ± lanceolate and irregularly dentate, a third to a quarter the length of the flower. **Corollas** 7–9 mm, often a very noticeably deeper pink, lower petal subspathulate and subacute at apex. **Fruits** 2·0–2·5 × 2·5–3·0 mm, distinctly wider than high, apex emarginate when viewed from the greatest width, but rather truncate when seen from the narrow side (Lidén 1986), periderm only slightly rugose when dry; 2n = 32.

Subsp. *officinalis* is the commonest taxon in arable fields, especially with spring-sown crops and potatoes, in allotments, gardens, other disturbed land and on newly-created road banks. An archaeophyte, its seed-bank may well be long-lived.

- var. *officinalis*. **Racemes** 20–60-flowered, **bracts** nearly as long as the fruiting pedicels, **corollas** 7–9 mm, purplish-pink, **fruits** 2·0–2·5 × 2·5–3·0 mm.

- var. *elegans* Pugsley. **Racemes** 30–40-flowered, **bracts** half as long as the slender pedicels, **corollas** 7 mm, pale purplish-pink, **fruits** 2·0 × 2·5 mm.

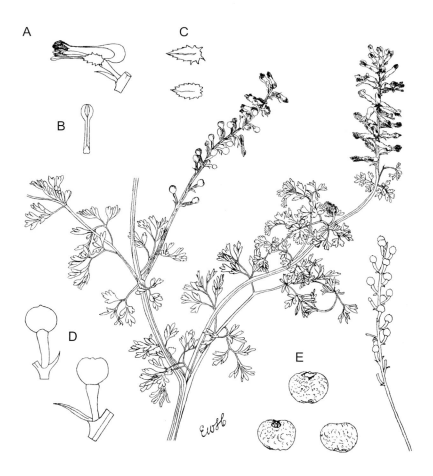

Figure 59. *Fumaria officinalis* (del. E.W. Hunnybun, edited from Moss 1920). A, flower. B, lower petal, top view. C, sepals. D, fresh fruits. E, dry fruits.

Figure 60. *Fumaria officinalis*, plants on new road verge, Enniscorthy bypass, Wexford, v.c. H12 (P.R. Green).

7b. *Fumaria officinalis* subsp. *wirtgenii* (W.D. Koch) Arcang.

Racemes (5–)10–20(–24)-flowered. **Sepals** 1·5–2·0 × 0·75–1 mm, irregularly dentate, smaller than in subsp. *officinalis* and not so lanceolate, about a fifth the length of the flower. **Corollas** 6–8 mm, sometimes paler in colour, with rather broad lateral petals and subspathulate lower petal truncate at its apex. **Fruits** 2·0–2·5 × 2·0–2·5 mm, not emarginate, often with a distinct apiculus, rounded in shape, periderm when dry more rugose than in subsp. *officinalis*; 2n = 48.

Subsp. *wirtgenii* is rarer than subsp. *officinalis*, and is commonest in arable fields on light soils in eastern England.

- var. *minor* Hausskn. More glaucous, the **racemes** 10–20-flowered, **sepals** smaller (1·5–2·0× 1 mm), **corollas** 6–7·5 mm, distinctly paler, though wings of upper petal are still blackish-red and **fruits** larger, 2·0 × 2·5–3·0 mm, and retuse at apex. It occurs mostly in South-east England (Sell 1998).

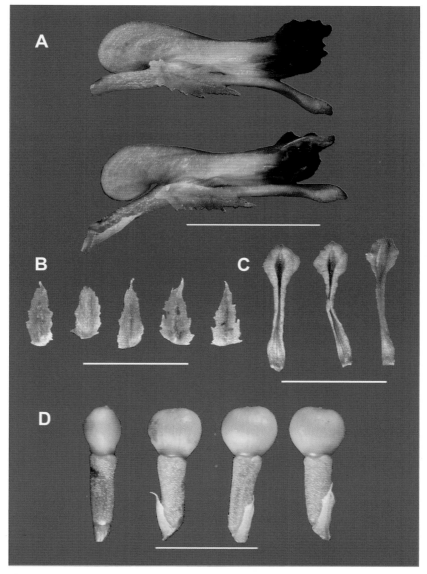

Figure 61. *Fumaria officinalis* subsp. *officinalis*, Royston, v.c. 29. A, fresh flowers. B, sepals. C, lower petals. D, fresh fruits (side view of left-hand fruit). Scale bars 5 mm.

- var. *wirtgenii* (W.D.J. Koch) Hausskn. Less glaucous, the **racemes** 5–24-flowered, **sepals** 1·5–2·0 × 0·75-1 mm, **corollas** 6-8 mm, deep pink, **fruits** 2·0–2·5 × 2·0–2·5 mm, rounded, with apiculus.

A European Southern-temperate species, *F. officinalis* is widespread in Europe and North Africa, and is widely naturalised outside this area. Its IUCN Threat Status is 'Least Concern' in Britain (Cheffings & Farrell 2005) and probably of 'Least Concern' in Ireland.

Figure 62. *Fumaria officinalis* subsp. *officinalis*, Campbeltown, v.c. 101.

Figure 63. *Fumaria officinalis*, Sandy Water Park, v.c. 44 (K. & R. Pryce).

Figure 64. Lower stem leaves of *Fumaria officinalis*; Royston, v.c. 29.

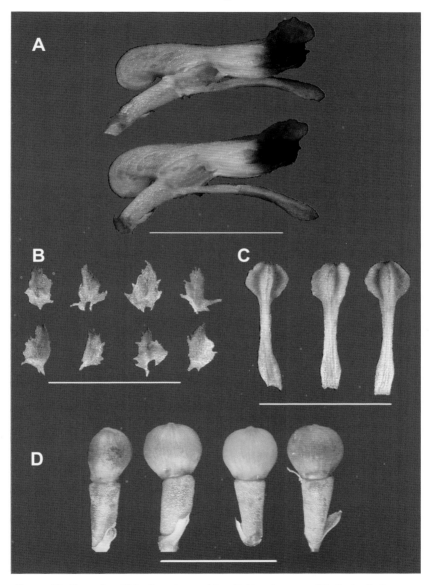

Figure 65. *Fumaria officinalis* subsp. *wirtgenii*, Royston, v.c. 29. A, fresh flowers. B, sepals. C, lower petals. D, fresh fruits (side view of left-hand fruit). Scale bars 5 mm.

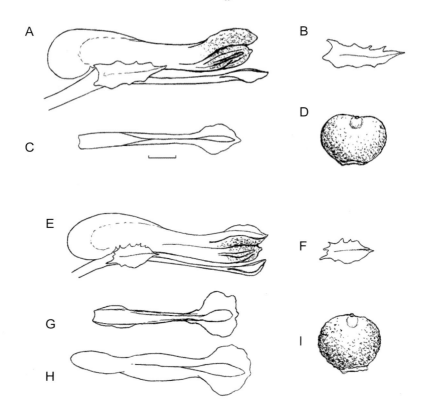

Figure 66. *Fumaria officinalis*. Subsp. *officinalis*: A, flower. B, sepal. C, lower petal. D, dry fruit. Subsp. *wirtgenii*: E, flower. F, sepal. G, lower petal. H, upper petal. I, dry fruit. Scale bar 1 mm.

Figure 67. *Fumaria officinalis* subsp. *officinalis*, garden, Campbeltown, v.c. 101.

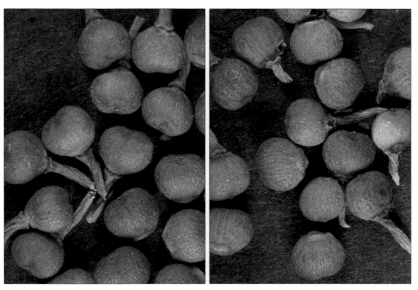

Figure 68a. Dry fruits of *Fumaria officinalis* subsp. *officinalis*.

Figure 68b. Dry fruits of *Fumaria officinalis* subsp. *wirtgenii*.

Figure 69. Distribution of *F. officinalis*, with increasing dot size for more recent records.

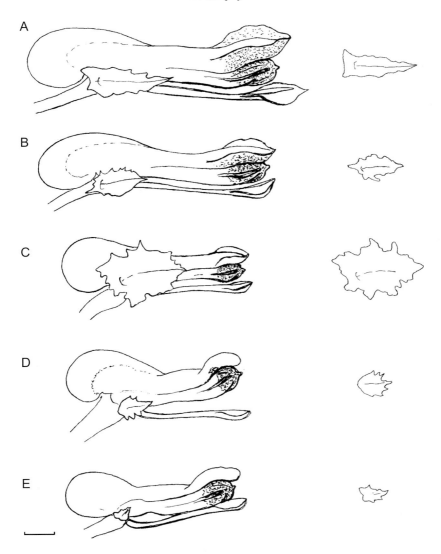

Figure 70. Comparative drawings of flowers and sepals of five *Fumaria* archaeophytes. A, *F. officinalis* subsp. *officinalis.* B, *F. officinalis* subsp. *wirtgenii.* C, *F. densiflora.* D, *F. parviflora.* E, *F. vaillantii.* Scale bar 1 mm.

8. *Fumaria densiflora* DC.

Dense-flowered Fumitory

Plant robust, weakly glaucous or green, branched from base, suberect at first, then diffuse, rarely climbing. Leaf segments usually channelled. **Racemes** (8–)15–30(–35)-flowered, dense (flowers extremely congested in bud stage), sessile to subsessile. **Bracts** sepal-like, slightly toothed, broad, white with pink tips, often much longer than the patent to erecto-patent thickened, fruiting pedicels, though occasionally shorter. **Sepals** 2–3·5(–4·0) × (1·5–) 2–3(–3·8) mm, nearly orbicular, wider than the breadth of the corolla, subentire to irregularly dentate, pinkish-white. **Corollas** 6–7 mm, short and broad with rounded spur, pink, wings of upper petal and tips of lateral petals blackish-red, lower petal subspathulate, margins patent. **Fruits** 2–2·5 × 2–2·5 mm, subglobose, obscurely keeled, rounded-obtuse at apex, small apical pits, indistinct neck, periderm rugose when dry; 2n = 32.

Fumaria densiflora is distinguished by the combination of relatively large, sub-orbicular sepals (2–3 × 2–3 mm) with small flowers (6–7 mm) in short, densely crowded inflorescences (Figures 71-76). The sepals can appear so large that the petals of immature flowers seem to peer out from between them (Spiers 2004). It is a very distinctive fumitory.

An archaeophyte, *F. densiflora* is most frequent in arable fields on the chalk of South-east England, but it may also be found in waste places, fallow fields and allotments and there is a second centre of distribution in fields enriched by calcareous sand around the Firth of Forth in Scotland. It often occurs with other rarer arable weeds in spring-sown cereals and root crops and its seed-bank may well be long-lived. It would seem to be less frequent than formerly judging by the decline in its distribution (Wilson 2002) but others consider its population to be stable at present (Braithwaite *et al.* 2006). Listed as 'Nationally Scarce' with a comment that its decline in recent years has been due to the routine use of herbicides and the application of nitrogenous fertilisers (Wilson 1994), it is interesting to note that it is ranked, on a threat basis, as of 'Least Concern' in Britain (Cheffings & Farrell 2005).

Widespread in the Mediterranean region, it extends north to Britain and Ireland (Figure 77). It is locally distributed in South-east England and eastern Scotland. It was last recorded in Northern Ireland in 1946 and in the Republic of Ireland in the 1960s (Reynolds 2002). Like some other arable-weed fumitories, it is classed as a European Southern-temperate species.

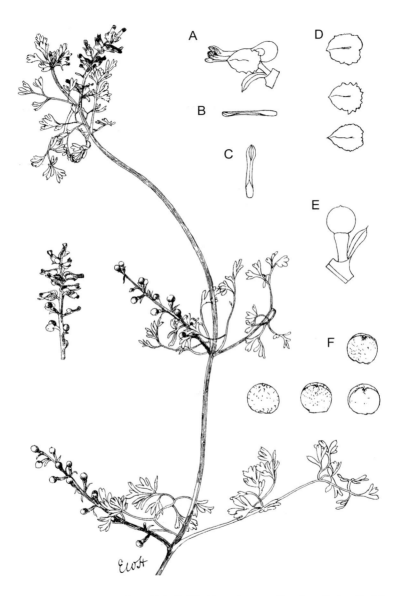

Figure 71. *Fumaria densiflora* (del. E. W. Hunnybun as *F. micrantha*) edited from Moss 1920). A, flower. B, lower petal, side view. C, lower petal, top view. D, sepals. E, fresh fruit. F, dry fruits.

Figure 72. *Fumaria densiflora*, Shorwell, v.c. 10 (G. Toone).

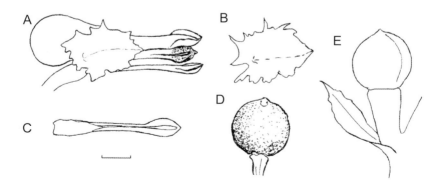

Figure 73. *Fumaria densiflora*. A, flower. B, sepal. C, lower petal. D, dry fruit. E, fresh fruit and bract. Scale bar 1 mm.

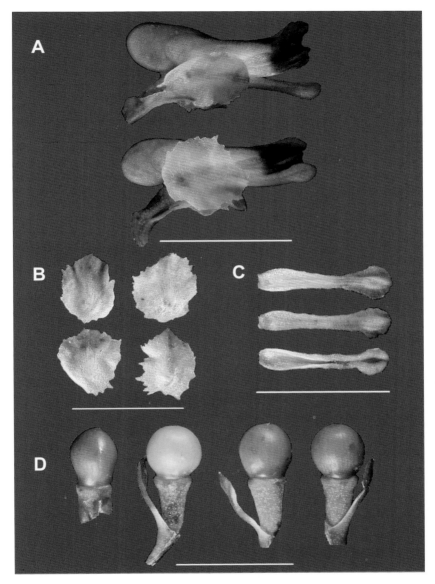

Figure 74. *Fumaria densiflora*, Royston, v.c. 29. A, fresh flowers. B, sepals. C, lower petals. D, fresh fruits (side view, left-hand fruit). Scale bars 5 mm.

Figure 75. *Fumaria densiflora*, Royston, v.c. 29.

Figure 76a. *Fumaria densiflora*, lower stem leaves, Royston, v.c. 29.

Figure 76b. *Fumaria densiflora*, dried fruits, Royston, v.c. 29.

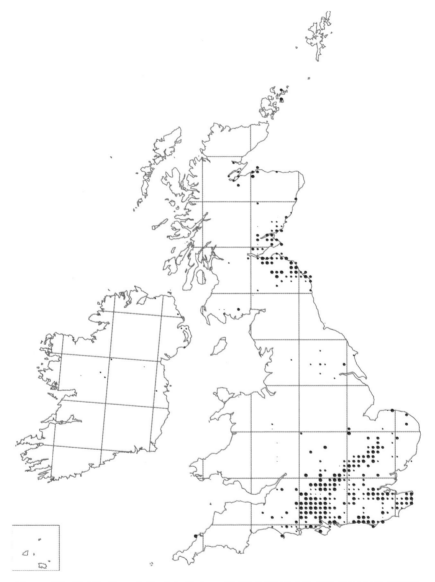

Figure 77. Distribution of *F. densiflora*, with increasing dot size for more recent records.

9. *Fumaria parviflora* Lam.

Fine-leaved Fumitory

Plant suberect to spreading, much branched from base, strongly glaucous. Leaf segments narrowly linear, channelled. **Racemes** 7–18(–22)-flowered, dense, almost sessile or with very short peduncles. **Bracts** usually broad, as long as or longer than the suberect, strongly thickened, fruiting pedicels. **Sepals** 0·5–0·75(–1·5) × 0·5–0·75(–0·8) mm, irregularly and often deeply dentate or laciniate. **Corollas** 5–6 mm, small, upper and lower petals white, but often flushed pink later, the wings of the upper petal sometimes with a dark blotch, lateral petals white, tipped blackish-red, lower petal ovate-spathulate with patent margins. **Fruits** 1·7–2·3 × 1·75–2·5 mm, but usually c. 2 × 2 mm, base narrower than the widened tip of the pedicel, neck indistinct, keel well-marked, apical pits present but obscure, apex variable, acute to slightly retuse, periderm coarsely rugose when dry; 2n = 32.

Fumaria parviflora can be recognised by its channelled leaf segments and glaucous appearance, combined with small (5–6 mm) white flowers with tiny sepals rarely more than 1 mm long (Figures 78-83).

When the flowers turn pinkish (cf. Figure 79), *F. parviflora* could be confused with *F. vaillantii* but that species has flat leaf segments and tiny sepals, never more than 0·5 mm wide and scarcely one tenth as long as the flower.

Three infraspecific taxa are accepted by Sell (1998):

- var. *parviflora*. Apex of fruits rounded-obtuse, with persistent apiculus.

- var. *acuminata* Clavaud. Corollas often pinkish, apex of fruits acute.

- var. *symei* Pugsley. Keel of fruits becoming drawn into a slightly notched beak as the fruits dry. Endemic to Cambridgeshire – up to 1994 there had been only one recent record (Wilson 1994), but this variety was noted again in 2008.

The Mediterranean *F. parviflora* var. *glauca* (Jord.) Clavaud, with more glaucous, shorter leaf segments and generally rosy-tinted flowers, has been recorded as a casual in Cambridge Botanic Gardens; it could occur elsewhere as a casual too.

An archaeophyte, *F. parviflora* occurs most commonly in arable fields on the chalk of South-east England (Figure 84), but it may also be found, at times, on disturbed soil where it acts as a colonist. Sudden appearances have been noticed on the Breckland following the clearance of chalk grassland (Petch & Swann 1968) and more recently after the construction of the

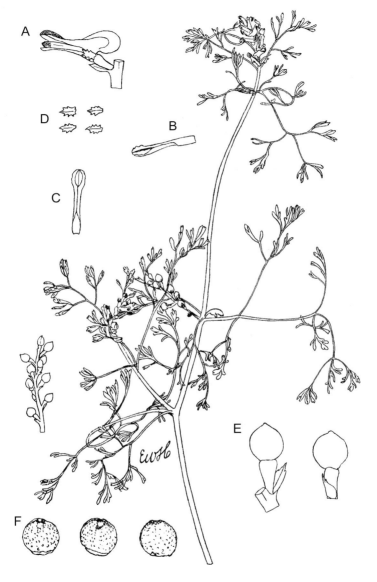

Figure 78. *Fumaria parviflora* (del. E. W. Hunnybun, edited from Moss 1920). A, flower. B, upper petal, top view. C, lower petal, side view. D, sepals. E, fresh fruits. F, dry fruits.

Figure 80a. *Fumaria parviflora* Lower stem leaves, showing channelled segments. Royston, v.c. 29. Scale bar 5 mm.

Figure 79. *Fumaria parviflora* (whitish) with *F. officinalis* (deep pink), Sherburn Wold, v.c. 61 (M. Foley).

Figure 80b. Dried fruits of *Fumaria parviflora* var. *parviflora*, Royston, v.c. 29. Scale bar 5 mm.

Brighton by-pass in Sussex in the 1990s (Spiers 2004), an indication of a long-lived seed bank. It is still, however, very rare and declining, presumably, as with *F. densiflora*, due to the use of herbicides and high levels of fertiliser. It is increasingly restricted to field margins where the effects of herbicides are less marked (Wilson 2002). Listed as 'Nationally Scarce' (Stewart *et al.* 1994), it is ranked on a threat basis as 'Vulnerable' (Cheffings & Farrell 2005). The only accepted Irish record was a casual from Cork Botanic Gardens in 1849 (Reynolds 2002).

A European Southern-temperate species, *F. parviflora* extends from the Mediterranean region through western Europe into Britain and is naturalised in both North and South America.

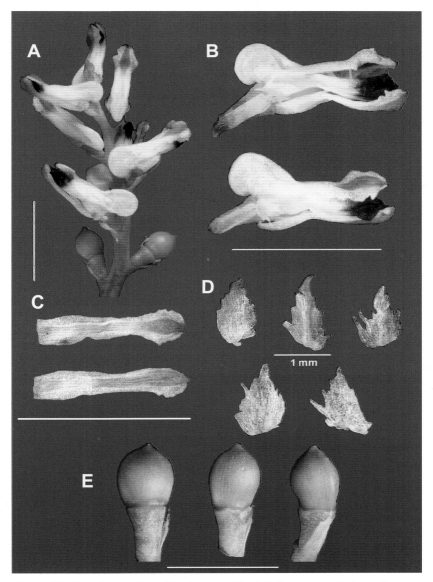

Figure 81. *Fumaria parviflora*, Royston, v.c. 29. A, inflorescence. B, fresh flowers. C, lower petals. D, sepals. E, fresh fruits of var. *acuminata*. Scale bars 5 mm unless otherwise stated.

93

Figure 82. *Fumaria parviflora* in arable field with poppies, Royston, v.c. 29.

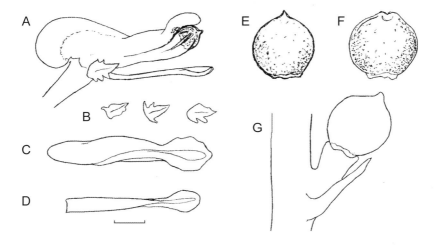

Figure 83. *Fumaria parviflora*. A, flower. B, sepal. C, upper petal. D, lower petal. E, dry fruit of var. *acuminata*. F, dry fruit of var. *symei*. G, fresh fruit and bract of var. *acuminata*. Scale bar 1 mm.

Figure 84. Distribution of *Fumaria parviflora*, with increasing dot size for more recent records

10. *Fumaria vaillantii* Loisel.

Few-flowered Fumitory

Plant slender, suberect to diffuse, well-branched from the base, ± glaucous appearance increasing with age, foliage sometimes sparse. Leaf segments narrow, mostly 1–2 mm wide, flat. **Racemes** (4–)6–18(–25)-flowered, lax, subsessile to shortly pedunculate. **Bracts** narrow, about half to three-quarters as long as the suberect or erecto-patent, thickened, fruiting pedicels. **Sepals** 0·5–0·75(–1) × 0·25–0·5 mm, extremely small, ± lanceolate, irregularly dentate, about one tenth the length of the flower. **Corollas** 5–6 mm, pale pink, upper petal subspathulate, often emarginate at apex, the wings of the upper petal broad and sometimes almost red, lateral petals tipped blackish-red, lower petal spathulate with patent margins. **Fruits** 2–2·25 × 2–2·25 mm, glaucous, subglobose, rounded or longer than broad, obscurely keeled, apical pits small, periderm finely rugulose when dry; 2n = 32.

Fumaria vaillantii can be distinguished by the combination of very small (5–6 mm long) pink flowers, the extremely small sepals that are hardly 0·5 mm wide and 1 mm long and the shape of the fruits, which are never wider than long (Figure 85-91).

Though the flowers of *F. officinalis* subsp. *wirtgenii* are larger than those of *F. vaillantii*, the two taxa can be confused, as their colour can be similar. This can occur particularly when subsp. *wirtgenii* var. *minor* is present as the flowers in this variety are only 6–7·5 mm, but the sepals reach 2 mm and the fruits are wider than long.

Two infraspecific taxa have been described for *Fumaria vaillantii*: var. *vaillantii* and var. *chavinii* (Reuter) Rouy & Fouc. (Pugsley 1912, 1920). The former is the common variety, the latter, distinguished by the reddish rather than the pale pink flower colour, has been seen only once in recent years (Wilson 1994). Neither variety is mentioned by Sell (1998).

An archaeophyte, *F. vaillantii* is one of the rarest fumitories in Britain (Figure 92). The only Irish record, from Cork, is doubtful (Reynolds 2002). Largely a weed of arable fields situated on chalk, it is rarely also found on disturbed ground (Rich 1992). It has never been common and is even less frequent now than it was. As with *F. densiflora* and *F. parviflora*, its decline in probably due to the greater use of herbicides and fertilisers in crop management. It is also less able to compete against the more modern, stronger-growing varieties of cereals and other crops (Wilson & King 2003). However, seed seems able to persist for some time in the ground and there have been instances where plants have appeared after a long time gap (James 1989). Listed as 'Nationally Scarce' (Stewart *et al.* 1994), it is considered, on a threat basis, to be 'Vulnerable' in Britain (Cheffings & Farrell 2005).

A Eurosiberian-Temperate species, *F. vaillantii* is rare around the Mediterranean, but extends north to southern Scandinavia and temperate Asia.

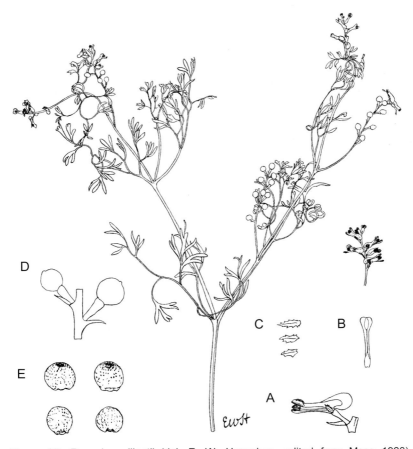

Figure 85. *Fumaria vaillantii* (del. E. W. Hunnybun, edited from Moss 1920). A, flower. B, lower petal. C, sepals. D, fresh fruits. E, dry fruits.

Figure 86. *Fumaria vaillantii*, plant in arable field, Royston, v.c. 29.

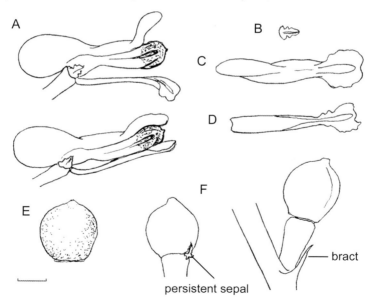

Figure 87. *Fumaria vaillantii*. A, flowers. B, sepal. C, upper petal. D, lower petal. E, dry fruit. F, fresh fruits, one with bract. Scale bar 1 mm.

98

10. *Fumaria vaillantii*

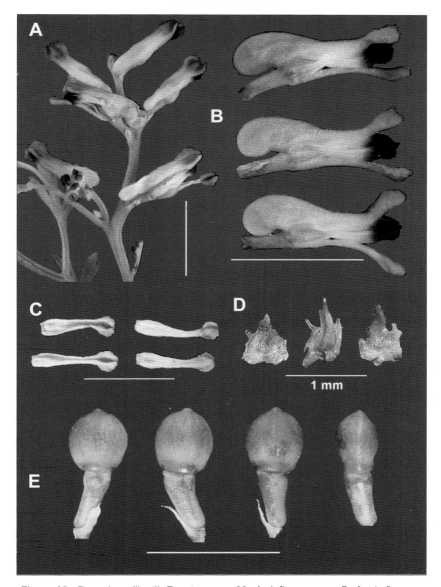

Figure 88. *Fumaria vaillantii*, Royston, v.c. 29. A, inflorescence. B, fresh flowers. C, lower petals. D, sepals. E, fresh fruits. Scale bars 5 mm unless otherwise stated.

Figure 89. Lower stem leaves of *F. vaillantii*. Scale bar 5 mm.

Figure 90. *Fumaria vaillantii* inflorescence, Royston, v.c. 29.

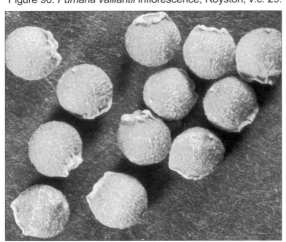

Figure 91. *Fumaria vaillantii* dried fruits.

10. *Fumaria vaillantii*

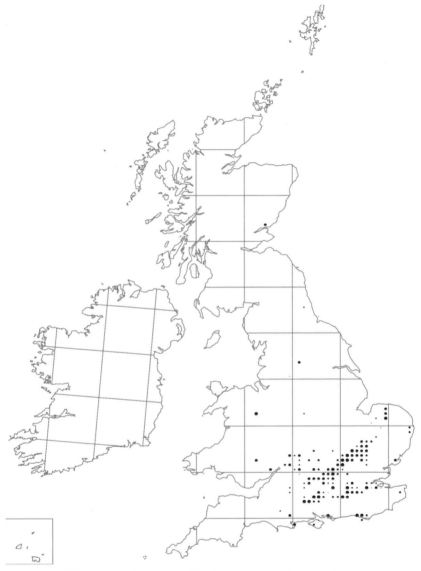

Figure 92. Distribution of *F. vaillantii*, with increasing dot size for more recent records.

Casuals

11. *Fumaria agraria* Lag.

Fumaria agraria is a plant of waste places, hedgebanks, gardens and maritime habitats around the Mediterranean, with the greatest number of sites occurring in Tunisia, Morocco, Spain and Portugal. It is a member of the *Capreolatae* (Lidén 1986). A large plant, it is capable of growing up to 3m, though often smaller. **Racemes** 14–25(–30)-flowered, generally much longer than the peduncles. **Bracts** about half to two thirds as long as fruiting pedicels. **Sepals** 2·5–5·0 × 1–2 mm, slightly dentate to subentire, ovate to linear-lanceolate, markedly narrower than the corolla. **Corollas** 12–16 mm, broadly winged, white, sometimes very pale pink. Lateral petals with blackish-red tips. Lower petal with wide, patent margins. **Fruits** 2·5–3·5 × 2·5–3·5 mm, strongly keeled, with emarginate apex, broad, shallow, apical pits and a periderm that is very rugose, almost tuberculate and shining when dry.

It is a plant that reminds one of *F. occidentalis* and, in one of its variants that grows in Tunisia, the wings of the upper petal are broad and ovate just as in *F. occidentalis* (Figure 93). However *F. agraria* differs in its larger shining fruits that may reach 3·5 × 3·5 mm, the narrower sepals rarely more than 1–2 mm wide and the very obvious, broad wings to the upper petal.

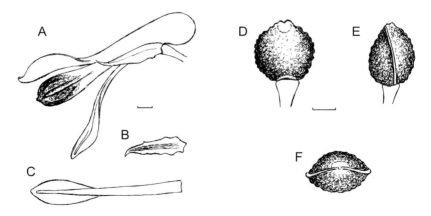

Figure 93. *Fumaria agraria* (Portugal, 2007). A, flower. B, sepal. C, lower petal. D, dry fruit – face view. E, dry fruit, - side view, showing strong keel. F, dry fruit – top view. Scale bars 1 mm.

In Britain the plant has been recorded on refuse heaps and waste ground, the first finds being made in August 1903 at Iver and Slough in Buckinghamshire and at Drayton in Middlesex (Druce 1904) (BM). Another record was made in 1939 at Dagenham in Essex (Wallace & Wilmott 1942; Jermyn 1974). It is a grain casual, with no modern records, but it could well appear again (Clement & Foster 1994).

12. *Fumaria caroliana* Pugsley

Fumaria caroliana is close to *F. officinalis* subsp. *wirtgenii* and Lidén (1986) places it under this subspecies. **Racemes** 10–15(–20)-flowered, lax and much longer than the peduncles. **Sepals** 1·5–2·0 × 0·8–1 mm, white, ovate and incise-dentate. **Corollas** 6·0–7·5 mm, upper petal whitish, though somewhat pink towards apex with broad, spreading, pale wings. Lateral petals blackish-red at apex. Lower petal slightly pink and obovate-spathulate. **Fruits** 2–2·5 × 2·5 mm, subrotund, slightly apiculate, obscurely keeled and rugose when dry.

Fumaria officinalis subsp. *wirtgenii* can be distinguished from *F. caroliana* by the slightly longer (6–8 mm) corolla with its deeper-pink colour and wings of the upper petal, which are blackish-red.

Known from northern France, only one plant of *F. caroliana* has ever been found in Britain, in a garden at Commercial End, Swaffham Bulbeck, Cambridgeshire, in 1996.

Hybrids

3 × 5. *Fumaria bastardii* × *muralis*

A single sterile plant was recorded at Cobo in Guernsey in 1914 by H.W. Pugsley. It was described as intermediate in character, the flowers being 9 mm long.

5b × 7. *Fumaria muralis* subsp. *boraei* × *officinalis*

Both sterile and fertile hybrids have been recorded for this fumitory. Records for the sterile form (*F.* × *painteri* Pugsley) are known from Guernsey, South-east England and Wales. The most recent of these is for a single plant growing by the roadside at Bryn-crug, Merioneth (v.c. 48). It was listed in 1972 by P.M. Benoit who noted, in addition to the subspathulate lower petal, that the pollen was mostly imperfect, good fruits were few, racemes were 15–19-flowered and longer than the peduncles, sepals measured 3·5–2·5 mm and flowers were 10 mm.

In 1896, similar plants were collected in Shropshire (v.c. 40) from a farm by Lea Castle, near Bishop's Castle, and again in 1907 from a site near Ironbridge, by W.H. Painter and determined by H.W. Pugsley. These plants had slightly narrower sepals, 3–3·5 × 1·5 mm, the flowers were 10–11 mm, and good fruits were present indicating that plants were fertile. The fruits were as wide as they were long, 2·5 × 2·5 mm, and truncate or emarginate at the apex, with a short but persistent apiculus.

7 × 8. *Fumaria officinalis* × *densiflora* (*F.* × *salmonii* Druce)

Highly sterile, this hybrid has been recorded from four localities in South-east England. The most recent find was made in 1972 when one plant was found at Five Knolls, near Dunstable, Bedfordshire (v.c. 30) by P.M. Benoit. It was intermediate in character with sepals like those of *F. densiflora*, but smaller 2·5 × 1·8 mm, and flowers 7–8 mm.

7 × 9. *Fumaria officinalis* × *parviflora*

A single sterile plant, considered to be this hybrid by H.W. Pugsley, was recorded from Mickleham, Surrey (v.c. 17) in 1910, growing with both parents. The plant had abundant racemes but no fruits. The foliage was like that of *F. officinalis* but small, the sepals were no more that 1·5 mm and flowers were 6 mm long.

Glossary

2n – diploid chromosome number.

Allopolyploid – a polyploid derived by hybridization between two species with subsequent doubling of the chromosomes.

Anthesis – variously defined as the period of flowering, the time of flowering, the opening of the flower or, more strictly, the dehiscence of the anthers with consequent shedding of pollen.

Apiculus – a small point at the apex of a structure such as a fruit.

Apiculate – with an apiculus.

Archaeophyte – an alien species recorded before 1500.

Arcuate – curved stalk shaped like an inverted U.

Bithecal anther – anther with two pollen cavities or sacs.

Caducous – falling off at an early stage.

Cleistogamous – flowers which fail to open, often small, pale poorly-formed. They are self-pollinated.

Concolorous – uniformly coloured.

Cuneiform – wedge-shaped, with narrow end at base.

Dentate – toothed.

Diffuse – widely or loosely spreading.

Divaricate – branches or pedicels widely spreading or greatly divergent.

Erecto-patent – branches or pedicels between upright and patent, spreading from stem at an acute angle.

Emarginate – shallowly notched at the apex.

Foliaceous – leaf-like.

Glabrous – hairless.

Glaucous – bluish-green or bluish-white.

Infraspecific – a taxon below the rank of species.

IUCN – International Union for Conservation of Nature.

Leaf-opposed – borne on a stem on the opposite side from a leaf.

Monothecal anther – anther with one pollen cavity or sac.

Neophyte – an alien species that has been introduced and recorded after 1500.

Patent – projecting outwards at right angles.

Pedicel – the stalk of an individual flower.

Peduncle – the stalk of an inflorescence.

Pedunculate – with a peduncle.

Periderm – fruit coat.

Recurved – curved backwards and downwards.

Rugose – wrinkled surface.

Rugulose – finely wrinkled.

Scandent – climbing.

Scarious – thin, papery, not green.

Self-pollination – applied to a flower where a stigma receives pollen from the stamen of the same flower.

Serrate – with sharp teeth, like a saw.

Sessile – not stalked.

Spathulate – spoon-shaped.

Sub-entire – a structure where the margin is almost lacking in teeth.

Sub-sessile – hardly stalked.

Taxon – a taxonomic group without a defined rank.

Tuberculate – bearing small, wart-like projections.

Zygomorphic – having only one plane of symmetry.

References

Braithwaite, M.E. 2000. *Fumaria purpurea* in the Scottish Borders. In Lockton, A.J. & Rich, T.C.G. *Fumaria purpurea* Pugsley in Britain. Consultation Report, BSBI.

Braithwaite, M.E., Ellis, R.W. & Preston, C.D. 2006. *Change in the British flora, 1987–2004.* London: B.S.B.I.

Castroviejo, S., Laínz, M, Lopéz Gonzáles, G., Montserrat, P., Muñoz Garmendia, F., Paiva, J. & Villar, L. 1986. *Flora Iberica. Vol. 1. Lycopodiaceae-Papaveraceae.* Madrid: Real Jardín Botánico, C.S.I.C.

Cheffings, C. & Farrell, L. eds. 2005. *Species Status No. 7: The Vascular Plant Red Data List for Great Britain.* Peterborough: Joint Nature Conservation Committee.

Clement, E.J. & Foster, M.E. 1994. *Alien Plants in the British Isles.* London: BSBI.

Crossley, J. 2005. Studies on *Fumaria purpurea* in Orkney. *BSBI Recorder* 9, 20-22.

Daker, M.G. 1963. Cytotaxonomic studies on *Fumaria officinalis. Proc. Bot. Soc. Brit. Isles* 5, 168–169.

Daker, M.G. 1964. Cytotaxonomic studies in European *Fumaria.* PhD thesis, University of Wales.

Daker, M.G. 1965. IOPB Chromosome number reports 4. Löve, A. & Solbrig, D. *Taxon* 14(2), 86-92.

Daker, M.G. 1981. In Wigginton, M.J. & Graham, G.G. (Eds.) *Guide to the Identification of some difficult plant groups,* pp. 13–15. Banbury: Nature Conservancy Council.

Druce, G.C. 1904. *Fumaria agraria* Lag. *Rep. Bot. Exch. Club Brit. Isles* for 1903, 9.

James, T. 1989. Germination of long-buried seed of *Fumaria vaillantii* in Herts. *BSBI News* 52, 27.

Jermyn, S.T. 1974. *Flora of Essex.* Colchester.

Jonsell, B. (Ed.). 2001. *Flora Nordica. Vol. 2. Chenopodiaceae to Fumariaceae.* Stockholm: The Bergius Foundation, The Royal Swedish Academy of Sciences.

Lidén, M. 1986. Synopsis of Fumarioideae (Papaveraceae) with a monograph of the Tribe Fumarieae. *Opera Botanica* (Lund) 88, 1–133.

Lidén, M. 2002. *Fumaria* L. In Strid, A. & Tan, K. (Eds.) *Flora Hellenica. Vol. 2.* Ruggell: A.R.G. Gantner Verlag.

Lockton, A.J. 2003. *Fumaria purpurea* in the British Isles. Unpublished Whild Associates report to English Nature. Contract No. CPAU03/02/182.

Margetts, L.J. 1988. *The Difficult and Critical Plants of the Lizard District of Cornwall*. Bristol: Grenfell Publications.

Margetts, L.J. & Spurgin, K.L. 1991. *The Cornish Flora Supplement 1981 – 1990*. Zennor, St. Ives: Trendrine Press.

Moss, C.E. 1920. Cambridge British Flora. Cambridge: Cambridge University Press.

Perring, F.H. & Sell, P.D. 1968. *Critical supplement to the Atlas of the British Flora*. London: Nelson & Sons.

Petch, C.P. & Swann, E.L. 1968. *Flora of Norfolk*. Norwich: Jarrold & Sons.

Pope, C., Snow, L. & Allen, D. 2003. *The Isle of Wight Flora*. Wimborne, Dorset: The Dovecote Press.

Preston, C.D., Pearman, D.A. & Dines, T.D. (Eds.). 2002. *New Atlas of the British and Irish flora*. Oxford: Oxford University Press.

Pugsley, H. W. 1902. The British Capreolate Fumitories. *Journal of Botany* 40, 129–136, 173–181.

Pugsley, H.W. 1904. A New *Fumaria. Journal of Botany* 42, 217–220.

Pugsley, H.W. 1912. The Genus *Fumaria* in Britain. *Journal of Botany* 50 Suppl. 1, 1–76.

Pugsley, H.W. 1920. *Fumaria*. In Moss, C.E. *Cambridge British Flora* Vol. 3, 177–190. Cambridge: Cambridge University Press.

Pugsley, H.W. 1924. *Fumaria muralis* Sond., var. *cornubiensis* Pugsley (nov. var. ined.). *The fortieth annual report of the Watson Botanical Exchange Club* 1923–24, 246.

Reynolds, S.C.P. 2002. *A catalogue of alien plants in Ireland*. Glasnevin: National Botanic Gardens.

Rich, T.C.G. 1992. *Fumaria vaillantii* Lois. in Dundee Docks. *BSBI News* 60, 66.

Rich, T.C.G. 2006. In Rose, F. & O'Reilly, C. *The Wild Flower Key*, pp. 116–119. London: Frederick Warne.

Rodwell, J.S. (Ed.). 2000. *British Plant Communities. Vol 5. Maritime communities and vegetation of open habitats*. Cambridge: Cambridge University Press.

Sell, P.D. 1985. A field of Fumitories. *BSBI News* 41, 16–17.

Sell, P.D. 1989. The *Fumaria bastardii* Boreau/*F. muralis* Sonder ex Koch complex in the British Isles. *BSBI News* 51, 24–26.

Sell, P.D. 1998. *Fumaria*. In Rich, T.C.G & Jermy, A.C. *Plant crib 1998*, pp. 67–72. London: Botanical Society of the British Isles.

Soler, A. 1983. Revision de la Especies do *Fumaria* de la Peninsula Iberica e Islas Baleares. *Lagascalia* 11, 141–228.

Spiers, T. 2004. In Harmes, P.A. & Sturt, N.J.H. (Eds.). *Sussex Botany*. Issue 01. Henfield: Sussex Wildlife Trust.

Stace, C.A. 1997. *New Flora of the British Isles* (2nd ed.). Cambridge: Cambridge University Press.

Stewart, A., Pearman, D.A. & Preston, C.D. (Eds.). 1994. *Scarce plants in Britain*. Peterborough: Joint Nature Conservation Committee.

Teesdale, I. 2008. Fumitories in Kintyre - and a species new to Scotland. *BSBI Scottish Newsletter* 30, 22-25.

Thurston, E. & Vigurs, C.C. 1925. Note on the Cornish flora. *J. Roy. Inst. Cornwall* 21, 455–469.

Wallace, E.C. & Wilmott, A.J. (Eds.) 1942. Plant Records. *Rep. Bot. Exch. Club. Brit. Isles*. 12, 265-307.

Wigginton, M.J. (Ed.). 1999. *British Red Data Books 1. Vascular Plants* (3rd ed.). Peterborough: Joint Nature Conservation Committee.

Wilson, J.B., Daker, M.G. & Savidge, J.P. 1990. A phenetic comparison of some *Fumaria* spp. (*Fumariaceae*). *Plant Systematics and Evolution* 172, 51-63.

Wilson, P.J. 1994. *Fumaria densiflora, F. parviflora & F. vaillantii*. In Stewart, A., Pearman, D.A. & Preston, C.D. (Eds.) *Scarce Plants in Britain*. Peterborough: Joint Nature Conservation Committee.

Wilson, P.J. 1997. The status, ecology and conservation of Martin's Ramping-Fumitory (*Fumaria reuteri* Boiss). Species Recovery Report for English Nature.

Wilson, P.J. 2002. *F. densiflora*. In Preston, C.D., Pearman, D.A. & Dines, T.D. (eds.) *New Atlas of the British and Irish Flora*. Oxford: Oxford University Press.

Wilson, P. & King, M. 2003. *Arable plants – a field guide*. Old Basing: Wild Guides Ltd.

Vice-county map and list

Key to vice-county numbers

1	West Cornwall	53	South Lincolnshire	105	West Ross
2	East Cornwall	54	North Lincolnshire	106	East Ross
3	South Devon	55	Leicestershire	107	East Sutherland
4	North Devon	56	Nottinghamshire	108	West Sutherland
5	South Somerset	57	Derbyshire	109	Caithness
6	North Somerset	58	Cheshire	110	Outer Hebrides
7	North Wiltshire	59	South Lancashire	111	Orkney islands
8	South Wiltshire	60	West Lancashire	112	Shetland
9	Dorset	61	South-east Yorkshire		
10	Isle of Wight	62	North-east Yorkshire	H1	South Kerry
11	South Hampshire	63	South-west Yorkshire	H2	North Kerry
12	North Hampshire	64	Mid-west Yorkshire	H3	West Cork
13	West Sussex	65	North-west Yorkshire	H4	Mid Cork
14	East Sussex	66	Durham	H5	East Cork
15	East Kent	67	South Northumberland	H6	Waterford
16	West Kent	68	North Northumberland	H7	South Tipperary
17	Surrey	69	Westmorland	H8	Limerick
18	South Essex	70	Cumberland	H9	Clare
19	North Essex	71	Isle of Man	H10	North Tipperary
20	Hertfordshire	72	Dumfriesshire	H11	Kilkenny
21	Middlesex	73	Kirkcudbrightshire	H12	Wexford
22	Berkshire	74	Wigtownshire	H13	Carlow
23	Oxfordshire	75	Ayrshire	H14	Leix
24	Buckinghamshire	76	Renfrewshire	H15	South-east Galway
25	East Suffolk	77	Lanarkshire	H16	West Galway
26	West Suffolk	78	Peeblesshire	H17	North-east Galway
27	East Norfolk	79	Selkirkshire	H18	Offaly
28	West Norfolk	80	Roxburghshire	H19	Kildare
29	Cambridgeshire	81	Berwickshire	H20	Wicklow
30	Bedfordshire	82	East Lothian	H21	Dublin
31	Huntingdonshire	83	Midlothian	H22	Meath
32	Northamptonshire	84	West Lothian	H23	West Meath
33	East Gloucestershire	85	Fifeshire	H24	Longford
34	West Gloucestershire	86	Stirlingshire	H25	Roscommon
35	Monmouthshire	87	West Perthshire	H26	East Mayo
36	Herefordshire	88	Mid Perthshire	H27	West Mayo
37	Worcestershire	89	East Perthshire	H28	Sligo
38	Warwickshire	90	Angus	H29	Leitrim
39	Staffordshire	91	Kincardineshire	H30	Cavan
40	Shropshire	92	South Aberdeenshire	H31	Louth
41	Glamorgan	93	North Aberdeenshire	H32	Monaghan
42	Breconshire	94	Banffshire	H33	Fermanagh
43	Radnorshire	95	Moray	H34	East Donegal
44	Carmarthenshire	96	East Inverness-shire	H35	West Donegal
45	Pembrokeshire	97	West Inverness-shire	H36	Tyrone
46	Cardiganshire	98	Argyll Main	H37	Armagh
47	Montgomeryshire	99	Dunbartonshire	H38	Down
48	Merionethshire	100	Clyde Isles	H39	Antrim
49	Caernarvonshire	101	Kintyre	H40	Londonderry
50	Denbighshire	102	South Ebudes		
51	Flintshire	103	Mid Ebudes		
52	Anglesey	104	North Ebudes	113 or S	Channel Islands

Provisional summary of vice-counties for which *Fumaria* taxa have been recorded

The following provisional lists of vice-counties for which *Fumaria* taxa have been recorded (pre- and post-1987, the latter in bold) have been compiled from the National Biological Records Centre database, the B.S.B.I. Atlas Updating Project, the literature and herbaria. Whilst the vice-county lists for species are probably reasonably complete, the lists for the infraspecific taxa become progressively more unreliable and incomplete depending on the extent to which they have been studied; the list is presented to stimulate further work. The vice-counties are mapped and listed on pages 110-111.

1. *F. capreolata*
    1a. subsp. *capreolata*: v.c. **S, 21, 29** (unverified records **4, 28, 45**, 47, **58**, 67, **72, 95, 99**).
        forma *speciosa*: v.c. S.
    1b. subsp. *babingtonii* var. *babingtonii* (records are generally assumed to refer to this variety): v.c. **1, 2, 3, 4, 5, 6**, 9, **10, 11**, 12, **13, 14, 15, 16, 17**, 18, **19**, 22, 23, 24, **25, 26, 27, 28, 29**, 30, 33, 34, **36, 37, 38, 39, 40, 41**, 43, **44, 45, 46**, 47, **48, 49, 50, 51, 52, 54**, 55, 57, **58, 59, 60, 62, 64**, 65, **66, 67, 68, 69, 70, 71, 72**, 73, **74, 75**, 76, 77, 78, 79, 80, 81, **82**, 83, 84, **85**, 87, **88, 90, 91, 93, 94, 95, 96, 99, 100, 101**, 102, **103, 104, 106**, 107, 108, 109, 110, **111**, H1, **H2, H3, H4, H5, H6**, H7, H8, **H9, H10, H11, H12**, H13, H14, H15, **H16**, H17, **H20**, H21, H22, H23, H24, **H27, H28, H29, H31, H32, H33, H34, H35, H36, H37, H38, H39, H40, S**.
        var. *devoniensis*: v.c. **3, 4** (unverified record for **37**).

2. *F. occidentalis*: v.c. **1, 2**.

3. *F. bastardii*: v.c. **1, 2**, 3, **4, 5, 6, 8, 9, 10, 11**, 12, **13**, 14, 15, 19, 20, 23, 26, 27, 30, 34, 35, **36, 37**, 40, **41**, 43, **44, 45, 46, 47, 48, 49, 50, 51, 52, 58, 59, 60, 62**, 63, **64**, 66, **67, 68, 69, 70, 71, 72, 73, 74**, 76, 77, 79, **80, 81**, 82, **83**, 84, 85, **87, 88, 95, 100, 101**, 102, **103, 104**, 105, **106**, 107, **108, 109, 110, 111, H1, H2, H3, H4, H5, H6, H7, H8, H9, H10, H11, H12**, H13, **H14**, H15, **H16, H17, H18, H19, H20, H21, H22, H23, H24, H25, H26, H27, H28**, H29, **H30, H31, H32**, H33, **H34, H35, H36, H37, H38, H39, H40, S**.

var. *bastardii*: v.c. 1, 2, 4, 19, **41**, **44**, 45, **46**, **58**, **76**, 101, **103**, H6, H7, S; this is the commonest variety but is under-recorded as it is the type variety.

var. *gussonei*: v.c. 1, S.

var. *hibernica*: v.c. **1**, **2**, 3, 4, 9, 34, **44**, **46**, 48, **49**, **52**, 59, 60, 71, **72**, 76, 100, 101, 103, **H1**, **H3**, H10, H13, H16, H18, H2, H20, H21, H22, H24, H25, H27, H28, H29, H31, H34, H36, H37, H38, H39, H40.

4. *F. reuteri*: v.c. **1**, 3, 4, 6, 9, **10**, 11, 13, 17, **101**, S.

5. *F. muralis*

    5a. subsp. *muralis* var. *muralis*: v.c. 3, 4, **8**, 10, 11, 13, 15, 17, 37, 39, 40, 49, 58, **59** (unverified records for v.c. **1**, 2, 5, **36**, 46, 60, 82, 85, 87, **89**, 90, 93, 96, **100**).

        var. *cornubiensis*: v.c. **1**, **2**, 5.

    5b. subsp. *boraei* (records are generally assumed to refer to this subspecies): v.c. **1**, **2**, **3**, **4**, **5**, **6**, **7**, **8**, **9**, **10**, **11**, **12**, **13**, **14**, **15**, **16**, **17**, **18**, **19**, 20, **21**, **22**, **23**, **24**, **25**, **26**, **27**, **28**, 29, 30, **32**, **33**, **34**, **35**, **36**, **37**, **38**, **39**, **40**, **41**, **42**, **43**, **44**, **45**, **46**, **47**, 48, **49**, **50**, **51**, **52**, 53, 55, **56**, **57**, **58**, **59**, **60**, 61, **62**, **63**, **64**, 65, **66**, **67**, **68**, **69**, **70**, **71**, **72**, **73**, **74**, **75**, **76**, **77**, 78, **79**, **80**, **81**, **82**, **83**, **84**, **85**, **86**, 87, **88**, **89**, **90**, **91**, **92**, **93**, **94**, **95**, **96**, **98**, **99**, **100**, 101, **102**, **103**, **104**, 105, **106**, **107**, **108**, **109**, **110**, **111**, 112, **H1**, **H2**, **H3**, H4, H5, H6, H7, **H8**, H9, H10, H11, **H12**, H13, H14, H16, **H17**, **H18**, **H19**, **H20**, **H21**, **H22**, **H23**, H24, **H25**, **H26**, **H28**, H29, H31, **H32**, **H33**, H34, **H35**, **H36**, **H37**, **H38**, **H39**, **H40**, **S**.

    The following varieties are under-recorded:

        var. *ambigua*: v.c. 3, 4.

        var. *britannica*: v.c. 1, **2**, 3, 4, 5, **9**, **14**, 46, S.

        var. *gracilis*: v.c. **1**, **3**, 11, 17, 45, **46**.

        var. *major*: v.c. **1**, 4, **46**.

    5c. subsp. *neglecta*: v.c. **1**, 2, 58, 77.

6. *F. purpurea*: v.c. **1**, **2**, 3, **4**, **5**, 6, 9, **10**, **16**, 19, 21, 23, 24, **34**, **35**, 36, **37**, **39**, **40**, **41**, 42, 43, **44**, 45, 49, **51**, 52, 58, **59**, **60**, 61, 62, 64, 65, 66, 68, **69**, 70, **71**, **73**, **74**, **75**, **76**, 78, **79**, **80**, **81**, **82**, **83**, 84, **85**, 86, 88, 90, **95**, **96**, **100**, **101**, 102, **106**, **109**, **111**, **H1**, **H2**, **H3**, **H6**, H9,

H10, **H12**, H14, H16, **H20**, **H21**, **H22**, **H26**, H31, H33, **H34**, H36, **H38**, **H39**, **H40**, S.

7. *F. officinalis*: as the subspecies are under-recorded, a list of all vice-counties for *F. officinalis* is as follows: v.c. **1**, **2**, **3**, **4**, **5**, **6**, **7**, **8**, **9**, **10**, **11**, **12**, **13**, **14**, **15**, **16**, **17**, **18**, **19**, **20**, **21**, **22**, **23**, **24**, **25**, **26**, **27**, **28**, **29**, **30**, **31**, **32**, **33**, **34**, **35**, **36**, **37**, **38**, **39**, **40**, **41**, **42**, **43**, **44**, **45**, **46**, **47**, **48**, **49**, **50**, **51**, **52**, **53**, **54**, **55**, **56**, **57**, **58**, **59**, **60**, **61**, **62**, **63**, **64**, **65**, **66**, **67**, **68**, **69**, **70**, **71**, **72**, **73**, **74**, **75**, **76**, **77**, **78**, **79**, **80**, **81**, **82**, **83**, **84**, **85**, **86**, **87**, **88**, **89**, **90**, **91**, **92**, **93**, **94**, **95**, **96**, 97, **98**, **99**, **100**, **101**, **102**, **103**, **104**, **105**, **106**, **107**, **108**, **109**, **110**, **111**, 112, **H1**, **H2**, **H3**, **H4**, **H5**, H6, **H7**, **H8**, **H9**, **H10**, **H11**, **H12**, **H13**, **H14**, **H15**, H16, **H17**, **H18**, **H19**, **H20**, **H21**, **H22**, **H23**, **H24**, **H25**, H27, H28, **H30**, **H31**, **H32**, **H33**, **H34**, **H35**, **H36**, **H37**, **H38**, **H39**, **H40**, S.

7a. subsp. *officinalis* var. *officinalis*: v.c. **1**, **2**, **3**, **4**, **5**, **6**, **8**, **9**, **10**, **11**, **12**, **13**, **14**, 15, **16**, **17**, **18**, **19**, **20**, **21**, **22**, 23, **24**, **25**, 26, **27**, **28**, **29**, **30**, 31, **32**, **33**, **34**, **35**, **36**, **37**, **38**, **39**, **40**, **41**, **42**, **44**, **45**, **46**, **48**, **49**, **52**, **53**, **54**, **55**, **56**, **57**, **58**, 60, **61**, **62**, 63, 64, 65, **66**, **67**, **68**, **69**, 70, 71, **72**, **74**, 75, **77**, **79**, **80**, **81**, **82**, **83**, **85**, 87, **89**, **94**, **95**, **96**, 104, **106**, **108**, **109**, **111**, 112, **H4**, **H5**, **H6**, **H11**, **H12**, **H15**, **H20**, **H22**, **H29**, **H34**, **H36**, **H37**, **H40**, S.

var. *elegans*: v.c. 10, 16, 17, **29**, 69.

7b. subsp. *wirtgenii*: v.c. **1**, **2**, **3**, **4**, **5**, **6**, **7**, **8**, **9**, **10**, **11**, **12**, **13**, **14**, 15, **16**, **17**, **18**, **19**, **20**, 21, **22**, **23**, **24**, **25**, **26**, **27**, **28**, **29**, **30**, 31, **32**, **33**, **34**, **36**, **37**, 38, **39**, **40**, **45**, **46**, **47**, **53**, 55, **57**, **58**, **59**, 60, **61**, 62, 63, 64, **65**, **66**, **68**, 70, 75, **77**, **80**, **81**, **82**, **83**, 87, **90**, **95**, **96**, 101, **105**, **106**, 108, 110, **H1**, **H3**, **H6**, **H11**, **H21**, **H33**, **H37**, H39, **H40**, S.

The varieties of subsp. *wirtgenii* are under-recorded:

var. *wirtgenii*: S, **29**, **46**.

var. *minor*: v.c. 1, 2, 3, 26, **29**, 31, 32, **34**, **46**, **65**.

8. *F. densiflora*: v.c. **1**, 2, **3**, **5**, 6, **7**, **8**, **9**, **10**, **11**, **12**, **13**, **14**, **15**, **16**, **17**, **18**, **19**, **20**, **21**, **22**, **23**, **24**, 25, **26**, **27**, **28**, **29**, **30**, **32**, **33**, **34**, **36**, 37, **38**, 39, 40, 49, 52, 54, 55, **61**, 62, 63, **64**, 65, 66, 67, **68**, 70, 72, **73**, 74, **75**, 76, **80**, **81**, **82**, **83**, 84, **85**, **87**, **88**, **89**, **90**, **91**, **92**, 94, **95**, **96**, 106, **111**, H17, H19, H21, H22, H25, H29, H37, H38, H39, H40.

9. *F. parviflora*: v.c. 1, 2, 7, **8**, **9**, **10**, **11**, **12**, **13**, **14**, **15**, **16**, **17**, **19**, **20**, **22**, **23**, **24**, 25, **26**, **28**, **29**, **30**, 33, 37, 39, 41, 53, 57, **61**, **62**, 64, 66, 80, 82, 83, 87, 92, H3.
   The varieties are under-recorded:
   var. *acuminata*: v.c. 14, 15, 16, 17, 20, 22, **29**, 30.
   var. *parviflora*: v.c. 9, 14, 15, 19, 24, 29, 62, 83.
   var. *symei*: v.c. **8**, **29**, 82.

10. *F. vaillantii*: v.c. 3, 7, 8, **9**, 10, **11**, **12**, **13**, **14**, **15**, **16**, **17**, 18, **19**, **20**, **21**, **22**, **23**, **24**, 25, 26, **28**, **29**, **30**, **33**, **34**, **35**, **37**, 39, **40**, 55, 59, 62, **64**, 66, 84, **90**.

11. *Fumaria agraria*: v.c. 18, 21, 24.

12. *Fumaria caroliana*: v.c. 29.

F. bastardii × *F. muralis*: v.c. S, **H21**.

F. muralis subsp. *boraei* × *F. officinalis* (*F.* × *painteri*): v.c. 4, 9, 15, 34, 40, 48, S.

F. officinalis × *F. densiflora* (*F.* × *salmonii*): v.c. 20, 24, 30.

F. officinalis × *F. parviflora*: v.c. 17.

The Botanical Society of the British Isles

www.bsbi.org.uk

The BSBI is for everyone who is interested in the flora of Britain and Ireland. It traces its origins back to 1836, when it was founded as the Botanical Society of London. From its earliest days it has welcomed both professional and amateur members, and it remains the biggest and most active organization devoted to the study of botany in the British Isles.

Information on the status and distribution of British and Irish flowering plants, ferns and charophytes is gathered through a network of vice-county recorders; this is the basis for plant atlases, county Floras and publications on rare and scarce species.

The BSBI organises plant distribution surveys, publishes handbooks on difficult groups of plants and has national referees available to members to name problematic specimens. Conferences and field meetings are held throughout Britain and Ireland and sometimes abroad. The society also publishes a scientific journal, Watsonia, and conference reports. Members are kept informed by a newsletter three times a year.

An education programme supported by the BSBI aims to bring high-quality botanical training within the reach of all, from A Level students to professional development and postgraduate courses.

Details of membership and other information about the BSBI may be obtained from The Hon. General Secretary, Botanical Society of the British Isles, c/o Department of Botany, The Natural History Museum, Cromwell Road, London SW7 5BD.

BSBI Handbooks

No. 1. Sedges of the British Isles – A. C. Jermy, D. A. Simpson, M. J. Y. Foley & M. S. Porter. Third edition, 2007, incorporating full accounts of 35 species of Cyperaceae and 47 hybrids in addition to the 76 species and subspecies of *Carex*. 566 pp., with descriptions, line drawings and distribution maps. A5 paperback.

No. 2. Umbellifers of the British Isles – T. G. Tutin. 1980, reprinted 2006. 200 pp., with descriptions of 73 species facing line drawings by Ann Farrer. Small paperback.

No. 3. Docks and knotweeds of the British Isles – J. E. Lousley & D. H. Kent. 1981. Out of print.

No. 4. Willows and poplars of Great Britain and Ireland – R. D. Meikle. 1984, reprinted 2006. 200 pp., with descriptions of 65 species, subspecies, varieties and hybrids of *Salix* and *Populus*, illustrated with line drawings by Victoria Gordon. Small paperback.

No. 5. Charophytes of Great Britain and Ireland – Jenny A. Moore. 1986, reprinted 2005 with a new preface and corrections by C. D. Preston. 144 pp., with descriptions of 39 species and varieties of Characeae (stoneworts), line drawings by Margaret Tebbs and 17 distribution maps. Small paperback.

No. 6. Crucifers of Great Britain and Ireland – T C. G. Rich. 1991, reprinted 2006. 344 pp., with descriptions of 148 taxa of Brassicaceae (Cruciferae), 129 of them with line drawings by various artists, and 60 distribution maps. Small paperback.

No. 7. Roses of Great Britain and Ireland – G. G. Graham & A. L. Primavesi. 1993, reprinted with corrections 2005. 208 pp., with descriptions, facing line drawings by Margaret Gold, of 13 native and nine introduced taxa of *Rosa*, briefer descriptions of 76 hybrids, and 33 maps. A5 paperback.

No. 8. Pondweeds of Great Britain and Ireland – C. D. Preston. 1995, reprinted 2003. 352 pp., with descriptions and line drawings of all 50 species and hybrids of *Potamogeton*, *Groenlandia* and *Ruppia*, most with distribution maps; detailed introductory material and bibliography. A5 paperback.

No. 9. Dandelions of Great Britain and Ireland – A. A. Dudman & A. J. Richards. 1997, reprinted with minor alterations 2000. 344 pp., with descriptions of 235 species of *Taraxacum*, most of them illustrated by silhouettes of herbarium specimens; drawings of bud involucres of 139 species by Olga Stewart and 178 distribution maps. A5 paperback.

No. 10. Sea beans and nickar nuts – E. Charles Nelson. 2000, reprinted 2003. 156 pp., with descriptions of nearly 60 exotic seeds and fruits found stranded on beaches in north-western Europe (many illustrated by Wendy Walsh) and of the mature plants (some with drawings by Alma Hathway), accounts of their history and folklore, growing instructions, etc. A5 paperback.

No. 11. Water-starworts (*Callitriche*) of Europe – R. V. Lansdown. 2008. 184 pp., with descriptions, line drawings by F. J. Rumsey and the author, and maps showing distribution in the British Isles and in Europe for all 16 *Callitriche* species and one hybrid reliably recorded in Europe; detailed introductory material, glossary and appendix listing the herbarium material studied. A5 paperback.

Other publications

Alien plants of the British Isles – E. J. Clement & M. C. Foster. 1994.

Alien grasses of the British Isles – T. B. Ryves, E. J. Clement & M. C. Foster. 1996.

Illustrations of alien plants of the British Isles – E. J. Clement, D. P. J. Smith & I. R. Thirlwell. 2005.

Plant crib – T. C. G. Rich & A. C. Jermy. 1998.

List of vascular plants of the British Isles – D. H. Kent. 1992.

Vice-county census catalogue of vascular plants of Great Britain, the Isle of Man and the Channel Islands – C. A. Stace, R. G. Ellis, D. H. Kent & D. J. McCosh (eds). 2003.

Change in the British Flora 1987–2004 (A report on the BSBI Local Change survey) – M. E. Braithwaite, R. W. Ellis & C. D. Preston. 2006.

Atlas of British and Irish brambles – A. Newton & R. D. Randall. 2004.

British alpine hawkweeds – D. J. Tennant & T. C. G. Rich. 2008.

Botanical Links in the Atlantic Arc – S. J. Leach, C. N. Page, Y. Peytoureau & M. N. Sanford (eds). 2006.

Current taxonomic research on the British and European Flora – J. P. Bailey & R. G. Ellis (eds). 2006.

Index to Taxa

Numbers refer to the taxon number given on the contents page, with the main page numbers in brackets. Synonyms are given in italics, and include names used in other literature.